Flying Blind

One Man's Journey Out of Darkness

by

Lou Briganti

All events described in these pages pertaining to the life of Joe Cory are true, though his name has been changed. The characters of Ron Brantley and his family are fiction.

ISBN 978-0-692-94496-7

To my mother and father

who taught me many things --

but most of all –

Self-Reliance

Foreword

Life challenges all of us, sometimes briefly, sometimes profoundly.

Joe Cory began life in 1934 in Allentown, Pennsylvania, a boy with all the physical and social characteristics of a Norman Rockwell portrait, quintessentially normal in every way.

The fifth child of immigrants from Syria, he is a second-generation American, a boy growing up in a working class town in a working class family, living for years in a neighborhood of houses with no central heat, but a kitchen tub for wintertime baths near the warmth of the stove. They lived through the Great Depression by working hard for every dollar and by devotion to the family Bible and the Syrian Christian Orthodox Church down the street.

Living through the decade of the thirties, young Joe witnessed the struggles of neighboring families who suffered unemployment and daily hunger, though his own father was always employed and there was always food on the Cory kitchen table at mealtime. Like all young boys in Allentown, Joe developed a serious affection for summertime popsicles and ice cream bars at an early age, and begging a nickel from Mom who didn't always have one handy taught him the value of his own paper route and the greater pleasure of popsicles bought with his own income.

At an early age, Joe was drawn to all things automotive. His curiosity about how cars and trucks worked became a fascination, and then a focus of his early education and later his career. The energy that drove him outdoors to play with neighborhood children as a youngster later drove him to work, first at his paper routes, then as a truck repair worker in a shop after school and on weekends, in Emmaus, a bus ride from Allentown.

High school taught him more about cars and trucks, and graduation led him directly to work in this area of his fascination. In all there was absolutely nothing about young Joe that was unusual. At seventeen he watched as American boys went to war in Korea after the long struggle in World War II, and he didn't need to be prodded to enlist in the U.S. Air Force, where his mechanical skills could be useful in aircraft maintenance.

It was then, shortly after his basic training and assignment to an Air Base in Illinois, that something happened to take Joe off the path he had drawn for his thoroughly normal life.

A series of excruciating headaches suffered at the Air Base took him to military doctors who quickly determined that he suffered from a combination of eye problems that caused the Air Force to give him an immediate, but honorable discharge. Less than two years later, nineteen year-old Joe Cory lost his sight.

Blindness made him suddenly helpless, a young man with a profound handicap who could look forward only to a life of dependence on a father nearing retirement age and older brothers and sisters who were busy starting their own lives.

The onset of blindness came with terrible swiftness, catching him entirely unprepared. The following pages are the story of his extraordinary reaction to this sudden shock.

Joe Cory is now eighty-two years old. A friend of many years has brought his young grandson to meet Joe and hear his story, in hopes that it will help energize and even inspire the young man to kick-start his own life which is presently stalled and going nowhere.

The youngster is fiction. Everything in this story about Joe Cory, however, is quite literally true. I've spent a long series of visits with Joe, listening to a story as only he and his bride of nearly fifty years could tell it. It amazed me, frightened me, and ultimately inspired me, as I hope it will you.

Joe asked me to add the following thoughts to this foreword.

This story of my life – well, parts of my life anyway -- are not meant to puff me up or make me into some kind of hero of self-reliance. Every day of my journey across the country, I owed heartfelt thanks to numerous people who picked me up, carrying me toward my destination, allowing me to sleep in their service station restroom, giving me directions, and a hundred other kindnesses. I owe even greater thanks for the help of Dr. Walter Brackin at Muhlenburg College, who overcame the College's resistance to admitting a blind student. To all the friends who have helped me negotiate the short journeys of each day and the longer journey of the life of a blind man, I owe more than I can repay.

Blindness shook me to my roots as a young man, and caused me to make a decision that was far more foolhardy than heroic. That I made it across the country as a blind hitchhiker is far less attributable to any bravery or intelligence on my part and far more attributable to the love and protection of a merciful God.

Chapter One
Dead in the Water

My name is Ron Brantley. I'm twenty-two years old, and I should be celebrating, but I'm not. I'm healthy, at least physically, but mentally, or psychologically if you prefer, I'm little more than a basket case. My college guidance counselor gave me a test that says I'm an introvert, which is likely. I know I'm shy, and over the past dozen years I've had few friends. Not none, but few. No girlfriends to speak of, though I'm not gay or even questioning myself about that. Unlike a lot of guys I've known, I haven't often thought with my "little brain."

I am the youngest of four children, the "baby" of the Brantley clan. My mother loves me, probably more than she should, as I have three sisters and being the "final child" and also the only male, I made her and my Dad really happy when I was born, or so I've been told about a million times.

My parents are good people, and they've been patient, both wanting me to be happy, productive, successful, and all the other good things that reflect well on their parenting. My sisters are good enough people, but to be honest they've always been a pain in the ass, primarily because they know everything and spent my whole childhood convincing me that I don't.

In a lot of ways I think I've become a pretty serious cynic. I've finished three years of college in four and a half years. I changed my major three times, moving from History to Political Science to Economics to Sociology and all four were intensely boring after the first courses. Being boring you can probably guess scoring "A's" was not in the cards. Right now attending classes is about as painful as getting a vasectomy with a butter knife, so I've taken a kind of sabbatical and come home. I just don't find meaning in any of it, and getting out of bed in the morning is something I avoid most days, though it's not much better in the afternoon.

My "situation" is totally intolerable – at least to others. By all normal measures you could say I'm "dead in the water," and what may be the worst part of it all is I just don't give much of a shit. My sisters are all paragons of success. All three have master's degrees, husbands, children, and a house in the suburbs of three different cities just far away so they only come home for short visits a few times a year. All of them are so happy and proud it makes my teeth ache, and I really don't even feel an ounce of sibling rivalry, so I don't know why I brought them up.

While they're both trying really hard to be "nice" about my "situation," my parents are suffering, personally and even socially. The reasons are simple enough. They have a 22-year old child who's come home. My very physical presence in their house is ruining their long-awaited second honeymoon. They should be running around the house naked and Mom should let Dad catch her every now and then. I understand all that, but right now I have no plans, no job, no money, and no purpose other than inhaling regularly.

Excuse me…I have to go take a dump.

I'm back!

Neil Diamond once wrote a song about "Searching for America." In it one of the lines said he was "lost between two shores…" only when he sang it, it sounded like he was saying "I'm lost between Toots Shor's."

I could imagine him eating meals at Shor's old restaurant on West 51ˢᵗ Street in Manhattan, but I don't believe Toots ever had a second place. If you're old and want to get a good cry, get on the internet and look up Shor's 1950s menu. The prices alone will make you weep, and my Grandmother says the food was actually good! Anyhow, I kind of feel like that…lost between restaurants…or between one breath and the next.

I know my father is getting impatient. He never spent a minute of his own life wondering what to do next, or so it seems. My Mom has "retired" from mothering and moved on to Granny-ing, except that she's bent herself into a pretzel trying to be supportive to me, and helpful and loving and sweet and patient and empathetic and….

…and it makes me sick. A few months ago she took me to a licensed clinical social worker named Cassandra Peele. That lasted about twelve appointments, twice a week. They wouldn't have lasted that long except that Cassandra was a total babe, maybe thirty, and hot enough to burn my fingertips if I could have touched her. Which I thought about a lot and grew angrier than cynical because I couldn't. Last week Mom made an appointment with a full-fledged psychiatrist, a sixty-something male with flowing white hair that he must comb for about an hour each morning before his hairspray goes on. He has practiced psychobabble and shrink-voice for forty years or so, and he's really good at it.

Two forty-five minute sessions later I was sent to our drugstore to get Effexor. Thinking my family is rich, Dr. Favenheim told me not to get the generic. I'm actually taking them, though I probably should just raid my parents'

3

liquor cabinet and get happy every few days for all the good Effexor is doing. He's given me more tests and because he believes in "non-directive therapy" he asks me what I want to talk about when I show up in his office. I try to furrow my brow and stroke my chin as if I'm thinking real hard about what I want to talk about. I can get away with it for almost 15 minutes before he "probes," and I have to admit there really isn't anything I want to talk about with him.

I should just tell Mom to relax and one day a lightning bolt will hit me and I'll wake up with a purpose in life, but she's so damned earnest about being helpful and forgiving and a hundred related etcetera's.

Anyhow, this has been going on for months now, and I'm not getting anywhere. I did apply for a job driving an Uber taxi, which lasted nearly two months on a part-time basis, but passengers started complaining. I wasn't friendly enough, they said. I swore to the supervisor that I never said the slightest inappropriate or unfriendly thing, but he fashioned himself a "business-builder" and he wasn't having customers complaining -- about anything.

One of the things I really haven't wanted to deal with is the rest of my family hearing about my re-invasion of my parents' honeymoon nest and my total fascination with drawing the next breath rather than doing anything else. Yesterday, however, was the end of that secret. Apparently my Dad had been talking to his father about me, and yesterday Grandpa Brantley came to visit.

He didn't waste any time at all. He laid a thunderous knock on my bedroom door at about 10:15 am and walked in with a hearty "Ron! Wake up! Breakfast is on the table!" I had a minor coronary.

It was true. There were eggs, bacon, even potatoes and coffee. I sat down in my bathrobe and took a sip of the coffee and poured some hot sauce on the eggs. He just sat there watching me, saying nothing. I felt really out of place eating, almost guilty, until he started himself. When we'd cleaned our plates, he whisked them away, refilled my coffee cup, and sat down again.

"So, young man, what's this about you hiding from life?"

Jason Whistler Brantley has always been a kind of giant in my eyes, especially when I was a child. When I was about three I saw him get angry at some family relative and he made a fist while I was standing next to him. It was huge. He had the biggest hands I think I've ever seen. As I think of those hands now and the stupid Presidential debates we had last year, I imagine he must have had something else that was awesome, but I'd never say anything about that for fear of immediate one-punch death.

He is one of those people who never say much, but when he opens his mouth, people shut up and listen. He doesn't engage in debates, and I'm not sure he's ever "discussed" anything at any length. He just says what he thinks, usually in very few words, and it doesn't seem like he's ever much cared if other people disagree with him. I didn't expect this day to be much different. To make things worse, his first question told me he wasn't happy.

"Uhh, it's nothing, really, Grandpa. I'm not hiding. I'm just trying to, uhh, figure things out."

"And that makes you so tired you sleep yourself silly. Either you're dumber – and lazier than anyone suspects, or it's a uniquely complex problem, this 'what to do with myself' mystery."

(Uh oh, he's more than unhappy.) For a minute I almost felt like crying even at twenty-two, but I inhaled really hard and held back the tears.

"Did my Dad ask you to get on my case?"

"I'm not getting into that. You know damn well you've got them both worried...more than worried. You're not twelve anymore. It's time to start being somebody."

"Yeah, well, I guess that's easier for some than for others." I was beginning to feel twelve, not twenty-two, and I was up a creek with no paddle and a leaky boat. Drowning was around the corner.

There was a long silence in which he stared at me with a very sharp focus and no empathy whatsoever...watching me sink. I was growing a really urgent need for a floatee...or maybe a trip to the bathroom, in Los Angeles.

Finally, he broke the angry stare. "I have someone I want you to meet."

That wasn't the kind of "floatee" I had in mind.

"Not another shrink, Grandpa, I've had two and they're a waste of time and Dad's money."

"He's not a doctor."

"What is he then, some kind of guru or motivational speaker?"

"Neither. Just an old man. But he has something for you to hear, and if you can rouse yourself to listen carefully enough, it might help you sweep the cobwebs out of your brain and become something more than a husk."

My eyes tried again to fill with water, and in the oddly empty center of my chest a flare of pain licked up like a sudden flame. For a moment the thought of suicide rose up in the flame and tried to sell me on the idea of self-immolation followed by sweet relief. I knew I couldn't share that thought with my grandfather or anyone else, and I had to admit it was really frightening. I swallowed a bunch of near-tears-mucus and it quenched the fire, but left me defenseless and incapable of resistance.

"OK, fine. Who is he? What is he?"

"I told you. An old man. Nothing more. Or a lot more. Depends on how closely you listen and how much you learn."

I sighed the sigh of the century.

"OK, fine... (again.) Where is he? Around here?"

"Not so fast, Ron. I'm not about to waste a moment of this man's time, or even yours. We need to get something straight first.

("Here it comes....")

"Tell me about honesty. What does it mean to you?"

(Hesitation. I hate trick questions.) "Telling the truth."

"How do you feel when you tell the truth about yourself?"

"I don't know what you mean, like right now?"

"Like right now."

"Well, since your arrival and since this conversation started, I guess I feel like shit."

"Good. You should. So for the moment, that's a pretty honest answer."

"Oh, gee thanks. So what?"

"So the antidote for telling hard truths that hurt is bullshit. It's what you've been trying to sell for quite a while. It needs to stop. Right now."

Sometimes even big-fisted grandfathers step over the line. Another flame licked up, but this time it was anger.

"Wait a damn minute! That's not fair. Maybe I'm confused, maybe I'm depressed, maybe a lot of things, but it's not all bullshit!"

His next statement came out of his mouth more softly.

"I didn't say it is." He paused for a second, as if my outburst actually made him stop and think. It tasted like a small victory. Sweet.

"I said sometimes the truth hurts, and when it does, we often want to run from it, and say things that hide the pain. We don't want to outright lie, so we say things that are horse-hockey, hoping people don't have a sense a smell. Before I introduce you to this man, you have to quit that, and I mean totally. Understood?"

Despite his softer tone, I felt like I was dropped into a blender, and the high-speed button had just been pushed. I really was lost between Toots Shor's. I opened my mouth to answer, but what came out was a really tiny voice. It was embarrassing.

"Yeah, OK."

Chapter Two

Joe

My grandfather drove me to the man's house. It was big. Money big. Brick and solid and spotless, not one, but two three-car garages with a second story above one, and what must have been guest rooms for half the town. I felt out of place.

When Grandpa knocked at the door I heard a man's voice inside call "Coming!" The door opened and there was the man, a smile on his face and his hand outstretched. It took me a second to realize he was reaching for my Grandfather's hand, not mine.

Grandpa took his hand and gave a hearty "Hello, Joe!" and introduced me. The old man took his hand back and offered it in my direction. When I took it, his handshake was firm, no dipstick strength contest, but firm enough to be surprising for a man who must be at seventy-five, maybe eighty.

"Come in, come in! Nice to meet you, Ron!"

"Thanks. You too, sir." It sounded kind of perfunctory, even to my ears, but I couldn't apologize, at least just then.

"Call me Joe. I'll have plenty of time for "sir" when I'm ninety."

"Oh! (a one-"huh" giggle) OK."

I thought we were all going to sit down together, but my Grandfather bowed out very quickly.

"You two talk. I've got things to do." And he was gone.

Joe led me down a flight of stairs to the home's walk-out basement level, which he had furnished as a pretty cool apartment for himself and his wife, while his daughter, son-in-law and a collection of kids lived on the two upper levels.

He pointed to a sectional sofa and I sat down. His wife came to say hello and asked me what I would like to drink. I thought briefly about asking for a beer, but it was still before noon, so I discovered the unusual-for-me good manners to ask for coffee or iced tea.

Joe settled down on the angled part of the sectional, close enough so that we could talk without shouting to each other, but far enough apart so we weren't invading each other's space. .

"So," he said. "I understand I should be telling you my story. I'm not sure what value your Grandfather thinks it should have for you, but that was his purpose in introducing us. Before I get into that, I'd like to hear a bit about who you are and…well, a bit of your own story."

I felt a twinge of discomfort at that.

"Joe, just tell me…what does my Grandfather want you to teach me?

"Nothing," he said simply. Too simply. Still, I wasn't ready to sit with this man waiting for my life to begin.

"You're not going to diagnose me and tell me what's wrong with me, are you? Are you some kind of sociologist, or expert in helping people 'find' themselves?

"Ron, I have no idea whether there's anything 'wrong' with you. As for expertise, in all truth I doubt I'm much of an expert on anything, except perhaps repairing a 1953 Packard Ultramatic transmission. From what little I learned from your Grandfather, I can only surmise he imagines you and I are similar people, with similar feelings and struggles, so perhaps you can relate to things that I've experienced in my life. If that helps you, I'm glad, but no, I'm no shrink and no teacher, and I have no interest in -- and no ability to psycho-analyze you."

I must have exhaled a long-held breath at that moment, and it occurred to me that he must have noticed it

Anyhow, I opened my mouth in a way that was way different from my pantomimes with social workers and shrinks.

"Joe, my folks…and now my Grandfather…are worried about me because they think I'm lost. In some ways, they're probably right. I have wasted a good deal of time trying to study things I hoped would be "relevant" and "productive" in my life, only to find out that they bored the crap out of me. The result is I'm twenty-two and I have no idea what I should be doing with the rest of my life, and I really don't even have the energy to continue my search for it. I like staying at home with my folks and sleeping until one or two in the afternoon and staying up watching TV or playing video games till three a.m. It's about all the excitement I can take.

"What's underneath all of that, I think I should admit, is I'm afraid. I'm afraid something is really wrong, for me to have no motivation, no energy, and no idea about my future. I've learned since I was a little kid that there are a lot of things I'm just not good at. I'm no genius, no part of an athlete,

11

and I sure as hell can't fix transmissions. It's probably not a stretch to say I feel defective…as a human being."

Joe sat there looking in my direction for a long minute, maybe two, without saying a word. Finally, his eyes dropped down toward his hands, and said quite softly:

"That's one of the most honest statements I've heard from anyone in a long time. Thank you. I think…given what you've just shared, that perhaps hearing my story might be helpful to you, but you'll have to be patient. It could take quite a while, surely more than just today, but I'll break it up into 'installments' to keep you from falling asleep."

The coffee arrived, and with it a plate of Mrs. Joe's chocolate chip and pecan cookies, still warm from the oven. After one bite, ideas of falling asleep left the room.

Chapter Three
Stumbles in Simulation

Joe sat further back in "L" of the sofa to make himself more comfortable.

"You know, Ron, you're not the first person to whom I've told this story. Your Grandfather has heard it, and perhaps another twenty or thirty people. I guess most of them found it useful, or at least unusual. A part of it is more than a little unusual, though the larger story is not much different than a few million others."

I sat very still, waiting for it to begin. I'm not sure Joe felt my impatience, but he seemed almost unsure himself.

"I think I should begin with some background. I was born in 1934, and raised in Allentown, Pennsylvania. It's near the eastern border with New Jersey, and north of Philadelphia. The town was surrounded by farms, and our house was small, no central heat, but a big wood and coal-burning stove in the kitchen, which was where we all took wintertime baths. My father, who came to this country from Syria, gave some initial financial help to his family back home, and worked at whatever he could find here. For a while he was a farm-to-farm peddler, walking to sell clothing and household items, whatever he could carry and sell. He also worked in a cement plant, and finally a steel mill. You could say we were 'working class' or even on the edge of poverty, so working and making money was everyone's responsibility from an early age. I had a paper route when I was very young, and even though I made very little, I saved almost every penny I made, and so did my two brothers and two sisters. When I was fifteen, I got a job as a mechanic's apprentice in a truck repair shop in Emmaus, working from 3:00pm to 10:00pm. The bus ride meant I didn't get home until nearly 11:00."

"But wait!" I said. "How did you know what you wanted to do? I mean you were only fifteen!"

Joe smiled. "Ron, try to understand how different things were back then. It really didn't matter what I did, as long as I was working and earning enough to help the family survive. Not working, not earning money, was just not a choice for any of us. Any job that paid regularly and wasn't immoral carried with it just as much honor and respect as any other. I suppose if I could have bought a few fancy suits and starched collars I could have dreamed about becoming an executive in some big company or maybe a Vice President in a big bank, but that was dreamland, especially at that age. I was glad even to have a paper route, and when I had enough money to buy a bicycle, I worked two routes, and made a little more."

"Anyway, there I was, growing up in this immigrant family, working hard and not thinking much about it. I was the baby in the family, with two older brothers and two older sisters. We worshipped at the Syrian Christian Orthodox Church, and we had an uncle living with us who was a priest in the church. Missing mass on Sundays was a serious sin, and thus not an option. Our family name, Cory, means 'house of the priest' in Syria, and my mother was very devoted to the Church.

I remember my parents quite vividly to this day. Both my father and mother were people with a strong sense of duty and obedience. My father was an early riser, who washed, shaved, and dressed in a clean white shirt each day before heading out to work, even when he worked in a steel mill. My mother kept our home spotless, tended to each of us children, and even baked communion hosts in our kitchen for Sunday services in our church. They took their responsibilities seriously and without question, and never once complained about a life of daily work, even though we had few luxuries to show for that work. I remember how happy they were when I was fifteen, and we could finally move into a newer house with central heat…and a heated bathroom."

I was listening carefully, but so far Joe's story was making me feel even worse about myself. I don't know how he picked up on that, because I was totally silent, but he stopped for a minute.

"Enough background, I think. I don't want you to misunderstand. Because we were poor, and even though many of the wealthier all-American families probably looked down on us, working hard from an early age was never a burden, and it was something we never questioned. With all of that, we were as happy from day to day, as anyone. But that was my family. Let me start on my own story."

Chapter Four

Polite Poverty and Ambition

"Let's see…where shall I start? I said earlier that I was born in November, 1934 in Allentown, Pennsylvania, in the heart of the Great Depression. My parents were immigrants from Syria, and while there were a few others in town, we were definitely an ethnic minority. My family was poor, but my father always had work of one kind or another, and we always had a home and food on the table. Still, I remember we were looked down on by some people, probably for the clothes we wore and things like that. I was the fifth of five children, the 'baby,' and a good bit of my wardrobe was pretty well broken in when it came to me."

Joe looked up and asked: "Do you know anything about the Depression?"

I thought for a minute, but shook my head. "I read about it in school, but the textbooks only gave us generalities, like people jumping out of windows when the Stock Market crashed in 1929. Oh, and I saw the old movie about the Dust Bowl out west, and the Joad family, from Oklahoma."

Joe nodded. "In 1951 I was a bit younger than you are now…I was sixteen and still in high school."

"Excuse me." I said, "Was that still in Pennsylvania?"

"Right. Allentown is just a few miles west of the border with New Jersey. These days some folks actually commute from Allentown into New York City. Our house was downtown, in a working-class neighborhood. I was taking a vocational studies program rather than the straight academic courses, so I spent a lot of time in shop classes learning to do things with my hands.

"Why did you choose that? Kids in my school who do that are gear-heads, and most of my friends assume those guys are just not smart enough for the college prep courses."

Joe was silent for a time. His silence made me feel like I'd just insulted him. I hoped I was just feeling the vibrations of the room.

"No-oo, Ron, I don't think I made that choice because I wasn't smart enough. Most of us in those days thought a good bit differently about the world and careers than we do now. In Allentown we all had…well, at least most of us had a pretty stark view of the world and how to get along in it. We didn't need famous philosophers to tell us that if we don't work, we don't eat. There were people in Allentown who went hungry and had to knock on our door and others, offering to work for a meal. The program I took in high school taught me several things I could do with my hands, and in those days we didn't have computers and robots to do things in factories and laboratories. Even before I graduated, I enlisted in the Air Force and was assigned to aircraft maintenance duty. My time in the service was very short, but I was really glad that I'd learned mechanical skills in school."

"Excuse me again, Joe…" I said, "…but what made you enlist? The war was over in the '50s, wasn't it?

"World War II was over in 1945, Ron, but the Korean War was demanding almost as many American boys, and serving my country was important in my mind."

Another momentary stab of cracks in my brain. It was clear that there is a price for being bored in high school history classes. I could feel my cheeks redden with embarrassment.

"OK, but then why was your service so short?"

Joe's voice relaxed, and my cheeks began to fade.

"It was just after I'd finished basic training and arrived at Samson Air Force Base in Geneva, New York and began to work. After a week or so, I came down with what you might call 'blinding' headache. It lasted a day and a half, and finally I went to the medical office to ask for some aspirin. The orderly asked me what it was for, and when I told him, he examined my eyes and sent me to the post's main medical building to see an ophthalmologist. It was there that Air Force doctors who examined me discovered that I had problems with my eyes. In those days there was little interest in keeping an airman on the government payroll for twenty years with those problems, so I was given an honorable discharge right away."

(Wow! Cool!)

"I wasn't too happy with that discharge. I was anxious to work on the aircraft, and believed I could do whatever I was asked to do. So I came home and decided to enlist in the Army. The only problem with that was the Air Force paperwork followed me faster than I'd anticipated, and the Army said "no thanks.""

I tried to imagine myself in Joe's position at that point. Even though I've never felt a desire to go into the military, especially in Afghanistan or Iraq, where I don't think we had enough business there to begin with, it occurred to me that he must have felt something like I'm feeling about myself now. Something way south of humble.

"Did that hurt, Joe?"

There was silence for a minute, and again I felt maybe I'd trespassed on some private part of his past.

"Yes, Ron, it hurt, because I really did want to serve my country when we were fighting what we thought was a just and necessary war. But it wasn't that simple. Mixed with the disappointment was a bit of fear about what was wrong with me. The Air Force doctors mentioned macular degeneration, which I knew little about, but those headaches were really awful and I'd never suffered them before.

"Anyway, when I got home, I had to find work. After a short time I got some help from my brother and father, who lent me enough money to buy a service station in town and run it full time.

"You *bought* a service station? I thought you said you were kind of poor."

This time Joe actually chuckled.

"Your history classes really were a bit shallow, weren't they? The station was already up and running for the past fifteen years, and we paid the much older man who owned it about $750. A few days after I began running it full-time, I also took time to go to my own doctor and even an eye specialist. The specialist said there was nothing that could be done about macular degeneration, which raised my fears, but my own doctor said not to worry. He said MD doesn't get really bad for ten, maybe twenty or thirty years.

"It was only a few weeks later when I was working in my service station and looking at a Ford repair manual and my customer noticed that I was holding the manual up against my face in order to read it. My personal brand of macular degeneration didn't take years to blind me. It took about three months. As my visual darkness spread, the doctors speculated that a case of 'devastating retinitis pigmentosa' may have contributed to it, but anyway, my case was highly unusual."

This time my "Wow!" was out loud. "You were suddenly all the way blind at like, -- nine*teen*? I mean...*totally blind*?!" It hadn't even occurred to me yet that Joe was blind right there in front of me, sitting maybe six feet away. Duh!! That attack of stupids made me really embarrassed, but even more just shocked.

Joe smiled at my slack jaw and wide eyes even though he could only "see" them with "other" eyes. I was about to begin discovering a whole mess of things about this man, and I think it was a long time before my own eyes relaxed.

"Before I start again, Ron, I have an idea. A good part of my story is about being blind. It might help for you to experience a bit of blindness, to help you understand. Would that be OK with you?"

I had no idea what he meant, but after a minute I nodded, then felt a flash of my own stupidity, and said "OK...what do you have in mind?"

He just smiled and got up from his chair and left the room. I watched him go and was surprised to see that he didn't bump into anything. He must have memorized the paths to take, the number of steps, just to get around without killing himself. A minute later he returned, carrying a little plastic sack. He sat back down in the same seat and handed the sack over to me.

"Here. Put these on. They're new and haven't been used yet. I bought them for my wife, who sometimes likes to take a short afternoon nap, but can't get to sleep easily in daylight."

I pulled out a black sleep mask, and did as he asked. When I had them on, I just said "OK."

"Good," he said. Are you totally 'blind'?"

"Yes sir, I really am."

"OK then," he said. His voice sounded as though he might be smiling, though I couldn't be sure. "Now, Ron, I'd like you to get up and find your way to the bathroom. Let me caution you, though. You'll want to move slowly...small steps...and keep your balance. You may bark your shins a couple of times, and I don't want you falling over furniture. It will survive, but I'm more worried about you!"

What felt like ten or twelve minutes later, and probably a dozen changes and reversals in my search, plus a few muffled exclamations of "ouch!, shit!, damn!," and so forth, I "felt" my way into his bathroom, which I later saw was only about twelve feet from where I'd been sitting. My "twelve-foot journey" was way harder than I could have imagined. I don't think I've ever felt like more of an incompetent than I did on that exercise.

I removed the mask to return to my seat with no more barked shins or incompetence. I was embarrassed by the smile on his face, and the barely concealed laughter, but I knew I deserved it.

Joe admitted that he'd enjoyed every stumble of my journey, but apologized for the chuckles and said I'd actually done quite well. Then his face turned more serious and he said something that really surprised me.

21

"You know, Ron, it might be a good idea for you to keep the mask on while I begin. It could help you 'feel' my experiences as you hear about them."

I began to feel something alright, but it wasn't comfortable; I was suddenly not bored at all, and more than a little anxious to hear more.

"Perhaps this little exercise has given you at least a hint at what I was feeling back then in late November, 1954. Tell me what you imagine, if you were in my shoes."

I suddenly wanted to think before I spoke. This was not a trivial question, and at least for the moment all my laid back cynicism had left the room.

"I'm not sure how to put this, Joe. I mean to have your sight, and all your senses, then to go blind so quickly, at that age, I imagine it must have felt like...like you were lost, like you'd dropped an arm or a leg somewhere and had no way to figure out how to start looking for it."

Before Joe responded, I felt something...a tiny suggestion, a "feeling" that he smiled before he spoke. When he opened his mouth a second or two later, the tone of his voice confirmed that little feeling. It was my first hint of something he would talk about a whole lot later in his story: the sudden, surprising discovery of other senses coming to life to help compensate for the loss of sight.

"It was that, and I'm afraid quite a bit more, Ron. At first, I remember feeling that the curtain had just come down, that my life was over. The blackness in front of my eyes was a great pit that I'd fallen into, and for me it was a pit of uselessness. My sense of shame was overwhelming. I had no purpose, no power to cope even with the littlest chores of life, and for what seemed like a long time, I had no sense of even being alive. Can you understand?"

I didn't want to, but I could. For one thing, I still had Joe's "blinders" on, so at that moment I was blind myself. More painful than that, however, was the whack upside my head of similarity between what Joe had just described and my own feelings of rudderless-ness, which were what brought me here in the first place. My head throbbed from the whack.

"Yes sir, I believe I do…understand."

"So you won't be shocked if I said that for some time I considered, and even "decided" in a way, that I wanted to end my life…."

"Well, I believe I can relate," I said, "…although suicide is an awfully big number, isn't it? I mean, even for someone with the lousy hand you'd been dealt?" (Listen to me, of all people, telling a man sixty years older than me that suicide isn't justified…like he should just suck it up and get out there and *BECOME* somebody! Suddenly my deodorant smelled like eau de hypocrisy.)

While I was turning up my nose at my own stink, (which Joe, fortunately, couldn't see,) he actually chuckled.

"As you can see, however, that 'decision' didn't stick!" Thankful for the relief, I joined him in the chuckle.

"After about three weeks of those dark thoughts, I decided to do something else."

"Wait, wait!" I said. "I mean, obviously you're still here and all, but what made you think going blind should mean you should check out, anyway?"

Joe dropped his head to his hands again, (as if he could see them…) and was silent for a time. In the silence it occurred to me that my question was a whole lot more invasive than polite, and I started to open my mouth to retract it, but my manners were too slow to arrive.

"I suppose…" he began, "…that my suicidal thoughts might have been a product of a whole set of factors. My family's 'situation' in the Allentown community, my own discharge by the Air Force, my Army rejection, my sudden unemployment, my sense that I was going to become totally dependent on my parents, who were no longer young at that point, and had little savings to retire on in the coming few years, I hope you can understand, it was pretty devastating."

I could understand, and I could also regret asking the question.

"It was also part of something I think I described earlier. The Cory family accepted that work was a necessary part of living, of surviving. Every one of us, we all worked from a very early age, and everything we earned went not for luxuries, but for basic needs. It was nothing like your life today, and please don't take that as a criticism of your family's situation. You have choices today that I just never had, nor did anyone in my family. Becoming a charity case, depending on my father to support me for the rest of his life, even though he had quickly promised me he would do just that, it was emotionally impossible, and on a purely practical level it was equally impossible. By the time I was nineteen he was sixty-four, and working in a steel mill in those days didn't tend to extend one's lifespan, especially as he worked as a chipper, which was both difficult – and more than a little dangerous. Who was going to support me after he was gone? Can you see how impossible it was for me to even think about that?"

I could.

"Joe, I'm sorry for asking the question. I didn't mean to…"

"Don't be sorry, Ron. The question was entirely legitimate, though it was also painful, but perhaps this is a good place to stop for today. Are you interested in hearing more?"

It was my turn to laugh. "I am, especially because you were about to tell me what you *did* decide to do, and I have no idea what that was, but I can guess it was a whole lot better than checking out!"

Joe smiled. "Today, I'd have to agree, although in the winter of 1954, the decision I made was entirely unreasonable, ill-considered, damn-near impossible, and entirely terrifying. But more of that next time we get together. How about tomorrow afternoon around three?"

Chapter Five

Desperate Measures for Desperate Times

As I left Joe's house after that first session, I began thinking that the old man had some real talents in story-telling, even in 'marketing' his story. That thought didn't call up my usual feelings of cynicism, however. I was actually excited for our get-together the next day.

As we took our places in his living room, Joe reached across and handed me the sleep mask again. He didn't see my smile as I put it on, and I have to admit I'm glad he didn't, because what made me smile was the thought that this was Joe's version of "Pokemon Blind."

Mrs. Joe came out again and spread a mini-buffet of afternoon snack-goodies across the coffee table in front of us. I lifted the sleep mask just long enough to watch as she took his hand and placed it gently at the edge of each of the small plates, naming the foods so he would know what he was reaching for. She hadn't seen me sneak a peek, because she then reached across and did the same for me!

"Just be careful with the wine glass," she said. "You have no idea how tippy it can be when you reach for it without your eyes."

I can't say that I'd ever given blindness much thought, but watching it play out right in front of me was quite a lesson. I suddenly began thinking about Mrs. Joe, and the obligation she had taken on many years ago to *serve* him in ways sighted men don't need. I'd already assumed that she had never known him before he'd lost his sight.

Anyway, we both picked at the buffet and made small talk for a few minutes, but after a short time of that I was more than ready for his story to continue.

"I think I used several adjectives in describing my decision, Ron, and I meant all of them, but at the same time I still believe, sixty-four years later, that it was a necessary one."

("OK, OK already! What was the damn decision?") I took a quick bite of chocolate-covered nuts to avoid saying that out loud.

"I decided to leave Allentown. To leave Pennsylvania altogether, and to get as far away as necessary, to a place from which I could be totally absent and anonymous to the neighborhood and all my friends and acquaintances, and from which it would be impossible to just give up and go home if I gave up on myself."

There was a long moment of silence after that sentence, in which I stuffed my mouth with buffet goodies and let the thought of his sentence sink in. In that moment my first thought was "gee, OK, I think I can understand that…matter of fact, what's the big deal?" Happily, I didn't give voice to that thought, and as I chewed he continued, obviously clairvoyant.

"I imagine you're asking yourself what makes that any kind of big deal, am I right?"

I swallowed too many half-chewed cheese-covered crackers, nearly choked, and gasped, "Well uhhh…"

"OK, I thought the same thought, right after I made the decision. It was the arrival of a hundred details that began to turn a simple flight from my sudden handicap into a really crazy idea."

I took a sip of the white wine that Mrs. Joe had poured into really nice wine glasses and regained my voice. "Like what?" I asked.

Joe smiled, warming to his own memories. "Well, let's see. I had already sold my service station, for more than $750 by the way, but most of that money went to pay off bills, and when I was done with that I had $28 left. I know my father probably could have given me a hundred or two more, and would have done so in a minute if I'd asked, but that was something I had decided in the first seconds of my desperation that I wouldn't do. So wherever I was planning to 'emigrate' to, I was going to have to get there on $28.

"OK," I said. "That makes it about impossible. (Duh!) Even in those days I'll bet air fares were higher than that."

Funny how you can say something and immediately feel stupid for saying it. If only we could feel stupid first, and not open our mouth. Of course air fares were higher than $28, and I didn't even know where he was planning to go yet.

Joe took a sip of his wine and smiled, as if he'd caught me in my stupidity and was already forgiving me for it. "You're right. No planes, trains or buses. I was going to hitch-hike."

I nearly choked again, although there was nothing in my mouth to choke on. "You were going to *WHAT*?!

"Hitchhike," he said, quietly.

Suddenly, I started to get it. A blind man…nineteen years old…three years younger than me sitting here…hitchhiking across --?

"Hitchhike to where, Joe? (My 10th-grade geography class kicked in…) Ohio?"

He shook his head, then spoke softly, little more than a whisper. "No, Ron. I'd decided to get as far from Allentown, PA as I could. I didn't have a specific town or city as my destination, but I was determined to get to the other coast any way I could."

My mind was swimming and suddenly the swimming pool had become the Atlantic Ocean, or more accurately, the Pacific.

"Wait, wait!" I practically shouted. "Didn't you say this was like November, or December?"

"Yes," he said simply. "As I recall, I left Allentown in about the third week in November."

"And you had twenty-eight bucks and weren't going to even borrow any more from family or friends?"

"That's right," he said slowly, watching has my eyes grew wider. He hadn't reminded me to wear the sleep mask yet, and right now I hoped he'd forget about that altogether. I mean my mind was racing and I felt like I was on a mini-board when the wave of the millennium appeared on the horizon, and I have never even surfed once.

"And it was probably colder than a witch's --?"

"It was."

"And you were stone blind."

"With the tiniest of exceptions, I was."

A thousand questions came crashing out of that killer wave and landed in my head.

"Pardon my French, Joe, but holy shit! How could you even think of trying to do something so…so impossible?!"

Again the smile as he thought about the question. "In one way it felt like an escape clause in a 'law' of Catholicism that had kind of stood in my way."

"What do you mean?"

"Well, you know the Syrian Christian Orthodox Church, like the Catholic Church, holds that suicide is a mortal sin, and the circumstances of suicide make it really difficult to do a deathbed confession and get absolution from a priest in the last moment of a life when I've just ended it myself."

He said this with a smile, and I guess it was the smile that lit a dim little light bulb in the recesses of my brain.

"So trying to do something crazy like walking and hitchhiking across the country in the middle of winter seemed like something I might be able to do, and if I failed, people couldn't exactly call it 'suicide'…."

I let loose a short laugh and he joined me in it – for a couple of seconds before losing his smile.

"But it wasn't a joke to me, by any means. Even as I think about it now, I remember that I had no idea whether I could make it all the way across America, and because I was still very fresh and feeling very 'injured' in my blindness, most of my brain was convinced that there were perhaps a hundred ways I might die somewhere along the way.

"I wrestled with the decision for days, even a week or two, but for me staying in Allentown and becoming a 'cripple' was just not an alternative. You might not realize this today, but in those days people didn't have quite the same attitude about 'disabilities.' Empathy wasn't a common word in people's vocabularies. Tolerance wasn't either. In those days if you were disabled you either stayed home with family members or you found yourself in state-run 'homes' for the 'deaf, dumb, and blind' or the mentally insane. Those 'homes' were far away from towns and cities, tucked away in rural areas were most people didn't have to encounter the inmates. Better for me to try to get away on my own resources and find some way to make a life as a blind man.

"Can you understand?"

It took a while for me to answer that question. He waited.

"I have to say...I mean I want to say…yes, but –"

"It's OK. I had the same hesitation, but the more I thought about it, the clearer it became. I just didn't have an alternative that I could accept."

"What did your folks say about it?"

"Well, I should tell you that I hadn't made a big deal about my eyesight among my own family members. I'd been living in my own apartment in Allentown while running my garage, and as my eyesight 'disappeared' as it were, I dealt with my first couple of weeks of blindness pretty much on my own. I sold the garage and my old pick-up truck, and got to work paying all my bills, even though that consumed damn near every dollar I had. I'd made up my mind to get moving without any more delay. It was already cold that November and getting colder.

"When I went home to tell my father I was leaving Allentown, he asked me "why?"

"I told him my eyes had gotten 'really bad' and that I'd sold the service station and just couldn't stay any longer. Actually, I'd already packed for the trip and my suitcase was by the front door. Again, he asked me to stay, and said he'd take care of me, but I couldn't agree to that. I wanted him to have his retirement.

"So he came to me and wrapped me in a great hug that lasted what seemed like a long time, then kissed me on each cheek. When he let me go, I asked my sister to drive me up to Route 22. She'd just given birth to her first baby and was living at home at the time while her husband was at sea with the Merchant Marine, so she actually broke into tears when we said goodbye as she dropped me off."

"OK," I said. "I'm gonna shut up now. I just want to hear what happened to you."

Chapter Six

Some Days are Stone

Joe settled back in his seat, propping his head against its
back. I couldn't take my eyes off his face. He closed his
eyes, as if he was going back into a dream, or maybe his own
time machine.

"The minute my sister dropped me off and drove away, I
remember my mind went into a kind of overdrive. I didn't
know whether to just stand there and stick my thumb out or
to start walking. That uncertainty was its own kind of
emergency for me, and in that mode my brain told my whole
body to start paying attention like it had never done before.

"I felt the ground beneath my feet. I was standing on a hard,
but gravelly surface, and my ears were kind of on fire to hear
passing traffic. I moved my feet, slowly at first, to find the
edge of the road pavement without walking into the path of
the next passing car. I decided to stay on the gravel
shoulder, but within a couple of steps of the road. I picked
up my bag with my left hand and prepared to turn to my left
and stick out my thumb with my right.

"I stood there for several minutes, but the sounds of passing
cars was just that – passing cars. No sounds of someone
slowing down and tires moving onto the shoulder. I'm not
sure how long I stood there, but I started to get cold, so I
dropped my thumb and began to walk. I knew I was heading
west, but that didn't help me relax much. I was just paying
so much attention to everything my senses were telling me

(except my eyes, of course. Actually they were communicating too, by tearing, telling me it was really cold, and the wind was coming from the west.)

"I'm not sure how far I walked, but it was probably a couple of miles, before I stopped again and put my thumb out. Traffic on the road had gotten lighter, and there were periods of a minute or more when all I heard was wind, so I moved a bit to my left so my left shoe was on pavement while my right stayed on the shoulder. It took me quite a while to start kicking myself for not packing warmer clothes, because I was still paying total attention to the information coming through my ears, feet, skin, and even my tearful eyes, which kept asking me to keep them closed to protect them from the wind.

"The second time I stopped to ask for a ride the same thing happened. Nothing. That didn't do much to build my confidence, but the rhythm of one foot on pavement and one on the shoulder began to seem familiar after a time. I even began to notice curvature of the road as my left foot lost the edge of the pavement and had to move a little to the left or right to regain it.

"The third stop to try the thumb was the charm, which was great because even walking wasn't doing much to relieve the cold. The sound of a car slowing down and pulling half off the road in front of me was exciting, which was almost dangerous, because I accelerated and nearly ran into the back of the car. I felt for the door handle and was suddenly unsure whether it was a coupe or sedan, so I had to reach forward for another door handle, which I found. When I got the back door open I lifted my bag onto the floor, wishing I had a way of knowing whether there was anyone back there.

Happily, it was just the driver and me, and he also didn't notice I was blind."

"Hold on, hold on!" I almost shouted. "Why keep your blindness a secret? You might have gotten rides sooner if you had one of those white canes or something to get you some sympathy!"

Joe smiled, but only briefly. "Ron, I don't want to pretend I had every aspect of my travel all planned and thought out. I didn't. Even now I'm not going to claim that all of my thinking and strategies were brilliant, but at the time I remember feeling more – more vulnerable than I had ever felt before. I wasn't sure just how some stranger might try to take advantage of me, but blindness made it seem much more difficult to take care of myself, or even defend myself, so I had decided to do my best to keep that under wraps as much as possible.

"Anyway, that first ride didn't get me very far. The fellow who picked me up was only going a few miles further on Route 22, and I was back on the road. At least I'd gotten warm, and I was thankful for that, even if it didn't last long.

"I went back to walking after that first ride, and I can say now that I don't think I've ever concentrated so hard, or paid more attention to my working senses, as I did on that first period of travel. It wasn't something I was accustomed to, and it took a lot out of me, even though I felt that paying total attention to everything coming through my senses was something I had to do.

"I walked several more miles that day. My sister had dropped me off just before noon, and as the winds picked up and it got colder, I began to suspect the day was ending. I

35

had a watch on my wrist, but it was no help in telling time until later when I pried the crystal off so I could feel the hands with my fingertips. I kept going until I got a second ride, which must have been several hours later. That ride gave me some progress, but after he dropped me off I had to walk again for a long time."

As riveted as I was, I couldn't help interrupting again.

"Weren't you getting hungry?"

"I was, and my hunger was an early sign that I hadn't planned very well. In fact I had neither food nor water with me, and I knew damn well that I couldn't table-hop across the country in decent restaurants on $28. It wasn't until I got to Harrisburg that I stopped to buy food and pick up a used bottle with a cap that I could use to store and drink water on the road.

"What did you buy? I asked.

"Two gourmet delights!" Joe said, a weird smile on his face.

"A loaf of white bread and a bottle of ketchup. Total cost was thirty-eight cents. My rough calculation at the time was that each loaf of bread and bottle of ketchup might last me three days, maybe four if I ate really lightly, so somewhere between seventy-four cents and a dollar and fourteen cents would last me a little more than a week.

"That's it?!" I asked. "Ketchup and bread? Nothing else? Damn!"

Joe smiled again. "Well you have to understand, Ron. In those days it was a common notion that bread is the staff of life, not the useless calories we see in it today. I was pretty confident that two or three ketchup sandwiches a day would keep me going. And after reaching Harrisburg I did have a refillable bottle of water. It was really dumb not to have thought of that. But I did add one more thing…"

"—and that was?"

"Hershey bars."

"Hershey bars?"

He smiled. "Chocolate was one of my favorite things in those days, and I guess it still is. A Hershey bar with almonds cost a nickel, so on that first shopping day in Harrisburg I invested one of my scarce dollars in a stash of twenty bars. The first two days after Harrisburg I ate two, and then I had to get serious, or they'd be gone in the first few days."

"White bread and ketchup? Ketchup sandwiches? And a Hershey bar. Damn!"

Joe smiled again. "I did say 'Spartan,' didn't I?"

My imagination was both frozen and on fire. It occurred to me that there is such a thing as being alone, and then there is being really, really, really alone. In the cold without protection, without money, without sight, and without wanting anyone else to know. Having no idea what lies at the end of my trip, or even if I would ever make it to the end of my trip. Watching Joe sitting across from me today, more than sixty years later, all warm and cozy, sipping his coffee, I felt a sharp sting, a needle between my ribs, or through my ear or in my chest, or wherever my conscience is. Here was a man, three years younger than me today, coping with the surprise of going blind, moving out on a journey I wouldn't attempt today if I had ten times the money he had then, and my full set of faculties and senses.

Joe took another sip of his coffee and closed his eyes, seeming to savor the dark roast and perhaps even the memories, but then a frown crossed his face, caused him to squeeze his eyes shut so tightly a tear fell from one of them. There was a lump in his throat as he continued.

"Harrisburg is about eighty miles from Allentown, but when I got there after two days and a few hours of riding and mostly walking, I felt worse than I have ever felt in this life. I didn't even realize that I hadn't slept a wink in those two-plus days. I had been in this steady state of total focus, total attention to everything around me, for nearly forty-eight hours, and once in the city I got totally lost, despite all that attention and focus. I was so hungry, so thirsty, so lost, that suddenly I felt like I had failed to achieve the one thing that meant the most to me, which was to avoid being a burden on my family. I had launched myself on a journey of two or three thousand miles and I had failed within the first hundred. I was so exhausted and so sorry for myself I couldn't take another step, so I didn't. I just put my suitcase down on the sidewalk and lay my head down on it and went to sleep. I don't know how many people had to step over me, thinking I was some sort of drunk, but asleep, I just didn't care."

I was starting to squirm in my seat, as if the needles were poking out of the upholstery, pricking me. I wanted to ask Joe is his wife had been doing a lot of sewing while sitting in my spot, but I didn't. I guess you could say I was relating.

Joe took a very deep breath, almost as if he hadn't been breathing for several minutes. When he resumed, it appeared that breath had done him some good.

"Anyway, when I woke up, which was several hours later, I got up and shook myself off. I had popped the crystal on my watch and checked the time, calculating back to the hour my sister had dropped me off, and deciding that it was still daylight two days later. I heard footsteps coming my way and reached out a hand.

"Excuse me," I said. "Can you point me to the nearest food store?"

"It turns out it was a man, and he probably hadn't seen me sleeping there, so he said 'if you go back the way I came, straight ahead for two blocks and turn right, the A&P is a block and a half down on the left.

"I thanked him and started off. I still didn't know where I was in town, and how to find my way back on the route I'd chosen, but I did find my way to the food store without any problem, and happily there was a service station half a block before the store, so I was able to use its rest room and even wash the sleep crust out of my eyes before going on. Once in the store I was able to get directions from one of the checkout clerks to the bread aisle where I picked up my first loaf of white bread and another shopper pointed me to the ketchup. Being as hungry as I was, the call of the Hershey bars reached out to me when I got to the cashier's aisle, so I added them to my bag. There was a woman ahead of me in line who had a few things in her basket, but who was also returning eight root beer bottles with screw tops to collect the deposit. For the two-cent deposit she sold me one, which I added to my own basket, and then filled it with water back at the service station. Altogether I began to feel a little bit better. I was learning that while I didn't want drivers who picked me up on the road to know that I was blind, it didn't matter as much about people in stores and on the streets in towns and cities where I needed help, or directions."

I shook my head as if I was clearing cobwebs. Joe's story was looming larger and larger in my mind, and I was feeling more of Joe's frustration and helplessness. Without even thinking much about it, I had reached down several minutes earlier and put the sleep mask back over my eyes. As I had guessed, it did wonders for my connection with what he was hearing.

"Did you begin to think, even though you were feeling a little better, that this whole thing had been a really bad idea?" he asked.

Joe closed his eyes and let a minute pass before answering. "Ron, I have to say there were many moments, and even hours, when I felt defeated, big-time, and really helpless, especially there in Harrisburg, only eighty miles from home. I discovered that in moments when I felt this way, my blindness itself made it worse – it made me feel profoundly alone."

I heard those words and felt them myself – I wasn't blind, for sure, but I suddenly realized that for me too, aloneness is an ugly feeling.

"But every time I began to think I should turn around and head back," Joe continued, "I was reminded about how much I didn't want to carry on as a cripple, dependent on family or other's charity. That alternative was never something I could tolerate. Even if I died on the road, or just survived the trip, it was better than that.

"Anyway, back on the road. I had to ask for directions two or three times to get back onto my route. I didn't mind telling people 'I can't see very well' and they were helpful. Finally I got to Carlisle, where I got onto the Pennsylvania Turnpike. In those days there were no signs prohibiting pedestrians, or perhaps it was just that when I was still seeing I paid no attention to them. I remember very vividly how cold it got. It started snowing almost immediately, and I'd lost my cap in Harrisburg, which made a real difference. I would have thought that I'd be picked up more often, but perhaps people were afraid of stopping on slippery roads.

"Walking on the turnpike was at least easier than walking in towns and cities, where I'd bump into light poles and telephone poles and stop signs and so on. I learned pretty quickly to try to anticipate obstructions rather than just walk into them, but I still must have looked like a village drunk about a hundred times.

"I think the thing that also helped to keep me going was the need to concentrate all my senses, more deeply and more continuously, virtually every moment that I was awake. I paid total attention to virtually everything I was doing, to every sound I heard around me, to feelings of temperature, to the sensations that came through my feet from the surfaces I was walking on, and so on. Believe me, it was a level of concentration and attention far deeper than anything I'd been called on to do when I had sight.

"It was exhausting at first, but as time moved on I began to get more used to it, and to improve my skills in a version of echolocation."

"What's that?" I asked.

Joe smiled. "You may have heard of it recently in a Disney movie – I believe it was called 'Finding Dory.' It's what whales and dolphins use to locate themselves and other things under water and track their direction and location. It's a kind of sonar, in which the whale makes a sound we can't hear, and then listens for the echo to come back to them, telling them where the surface is, where the ocean floor is, etc."

"So you learned how to use 'human sonar'?

"In a way, yes. For example, I listened to the sounds of vehicles moving along the roads. With my background as a mechanic, I found I could identify almost all vehicles accurately just by the sound of their engines. I began to determine how far from me they were when I could first hear them, which direction they were going, and even how fast they were moving. As you can imagine, walking on the edge of the road, with one foot on the pavement and one on the shoulder, I really needed that skill just to avoid getting hit and killed."

I could imagine. With Joe's sleep mask on, I could imagine only too vividly. I shivered.

"Of course I could hear if a vehicle slowed down and stopped when I had my thumb out, and I'd know what kind of vehicle it was. But it wasn't just sounds I had to pay attention to. As I continued my trip I found myself noticing where the sun was, at least on sunny days, by even the smallest differences in temperature on my skin. That became a second way to tell time, at least approximately. I felt the wind, of course, and snow, and knowing that most of the weather in the eastern part of the country came from the west, I could begin to track the direction I was walking pretty accurately by the way the wind was hitting my face. I could hear occasional animal sounds in the woods to my right, and you know I paid close attention to those. Getting mauled by a bear or mountain cat was not my most desirable way to end my life. I found I even had to pay close attention at times to the absence of sounds, and learn from that as well."

I was imagining a bit too vividly. I felt as though I was walking alongside Joe, and I developed a sudden longing for my parents' nice warm house and even my nice warm bed.

"OK," I said. "So you're developing your own 'sonar.' I can understand how alert you had to be. It must have been exhausting. What kind of other things were you learning?" I took off the sleep mask. It made things almost too vivid for me, almost like virtual reality. When I had my sight back, Joe was smiling at my last question.

"I discovered pretty quickly that when a driver would pick me up, he would want me to stay awake, even though being exhausted and suddenly warming up made me really sleepy. I would have been grateful as anything for an hour or two of sleep, but many of the drivers who picked me up had their own drowsiness problems and wanted my help and conversation to stay awake themselves.

"At night, when one driver dropped me off at a point where he was getting off the turnpike, I asked him to point me to a billboard somewhere nearby, and happily there was one not too far off. Billboards were really important for me, especially the farther I got, because even in the dead of winter I was more afraid of the dead of snakebites, and if I could get to the billboard and climb up on its walkway the men would use to paste up a new advertisement, and sleep ten feet off the ground, I imagined that most snakes couldn't climb, or even if they could, they would want to stay underground in that cold, so I'd be alive the next morning. Because I couldn't 'see' the billboard, I began listening for the sounds its structure would make as it creaked in the wind. That wind made it tough though, because it seemed always to blow up between the boards under me, so most nights I did my best to squeeze myself into a little ball and lie on top of my suitcase to get some protection from the cold.

"The billboards became a first choice for sleeping places if I was not in a town somewhere, but they presented another problem as well. Many of them were as far as a hundred yards from the road way, and several times I got lost either getting to them, or getting back to the road in the morning. When that happened, I became really frightened, even as I remember it now. Getting lost in the woods away from the road I'd been on was really frightening for me, almost to the point of panic. The first time it happened was near Pittsburgh. It was in those moments that my fear was almost paralyzing. I remember praying, sitting on my suitcase, far from any road, with tears running down my cheeks, asking 'where am I, God? And where are you?' I felt utterly helpless and I had no idea how long I would be lost, or where I would be when I found a road again. An hour, or several hours later, when I did find a road, I was overjoyed, but I had no idea that it was the road I'd been on the previous evening.

"As I got nearer to Pittsburg the snow began getting deeper and walking got harder. With my pop-off watch crystal I could tell time by touching the watch hands very gently, but I no longer knew whether it was AM or PM, night or day. There were other clues, of course, like lower volumes of traffic sounds at night and lower temperatures, but those were about my only clues.

"From Pittsburg to the Ohio border I had to walk most of the way, which was hard, but I was learning things all the time. My background in the auto repair business helped me to tell one oncoming car from another just by its engine sound. I was also getting better and better at telling where I was by the messages I was getting through my feet. In the beginning, I had to be careful not to wander off the road, because finding my way back might be difficult. It took me awhile to learn to use my hearing in ways I never had before.

"Echolocation was a really critical skill for me, even later when I was driving a car."

"You were *what*?!

"Driving a car, but that came much later. Anyway, echolocation became very important to me throughout my trip. I didn't develop this skill all at once, but it first became useful, and then critical as my travel continued. I have to admit, though, that as I walked and hitchhiked through Ohio, snow made echo-location more difficult. It muffled most sounds, and also disguised the sensory messages to my foot soles.

"I got tangled in woods and bushes a few times as I was making for a roadside billboard, and when I was walking in towns and cities, I also walked into a few poles, speed limit signposts and other signs announcing exits and so on. I was fortunate not to hurt myself seriously, but if there were witnesses, they must have thought I was drunk."

I had listened through this testimony without interruption, but not without my own feelings about what I was hearing. Now that I was wearing the sleep mask again, I was experiencing my own reactions to the situations Joe was describing as if I was the one in the story. They were not small reactions.

"Let me stop you for a minute, Joe. I'm wearing the sleep mask again, if you didn't notice, and I feel like I'm walking with you. It's not a good feeling, and I guess it would be fair to say I'm kind of getting overwhelmed. Just listening to your voice, it's difficult to sense how frightened you were, even days after you started, but in my imagination, even though I was making progress in terms of miles from home, I'd be more frightened than ever. Weren't you?"

Joe thought about that for a moment before responding.

"As I think about it, almost every time I have told any of the details of this trip across the country, different things have come to mind. Not all of them are pleasant, either. I know that as I walked along the roads, between rides, I felt more alone than I have ever felt, almost as if I was walking in a box of darkness, and the world was outside of it. I imagined many times that the box was also invisible to others, and so was I, walking within it. Many times as I made my way through Ohio the cold was bad enough to make me pretty sure I'd freeze to death, so I was afraid of that as well. Then there was snakes. I had been hugely frightened of snakes since I was a small boy. It was silly in a way, because I was educated enough to know that in the dead of winter snakes hibernate underground, and I had little to fear, at least in the

46

north, but on the few nights when I could find no billboards to climb onto, I had to curl up under a tree or bush and sleep on the ground. I did lie on the ground in those nights, but I doubt I ever got any sleep."

"On the other hand, whenever my fears rose up to a near-panic level, and there were a few times when they seemed great enough to stop me, mostly when I was walking, or getting lost, I did just that. I stopped and stood very still. In those times it took a few moments for a couple of things to happen. One was that my brain slowed down. It took only a minute or two, and in that time I got very quiet, and started paying attention to my senses again. As long as I was near a road, even with light traffic, that sound reminded me that I wasn't quite as alone as I'd felt, though on other 'lost' occasions, the world around me was silent, which was much worse. As I stood still in those moments, I also felt the cold grow more intense, and the urge to walk just to fight the cold grew. On a couple of occasions I also thought about alternatives. Like just lying down and waiting to die, or getting somewhere where I could beg someone to lend me enough money to get a bus back to Allentown and surrender. I could even walk out into the middle of the road and wait to get run over. That thought, of course, led to imagining an eternity in hell, and although the heat of a nice fire might have been a temptation, I shuddered at the prospect of that kind of eternity."

I'd listened to this, and though I understood, and even agreed with Joe's reasoning, I'm not sure if my own brain would have been as much help as his was to him. I certainly wouldn't have his sense of 'gallows' humor about it.

We stopped his story at that point, and I took off the sleep mask, glad to find the light of day again. We arranged to continue two days later, and I went home, exhausted. Funny thing, though. When I got home I couldn't sleep. I couldn't get it up for video games or TV either. I just sat in my game chair and closed my eyes…and saw a snow-covered road leading somewhere…I wasn't sure where.

Chapter Seven

Snowfall

Joe's wife Jackie answered the door with a smile that had become familiar, and increasingly amazing to me. She ushered me downstairs to find Joe sitting at his kitchen table, where Jackie had laid out a mini-smorgasbord of edibles. I guessed she had already acquainted Joe with their placement on the table so he could make 'braille' selections as his narrative went along, so I was careful not to move the dishes when I selected my own bites.

After greetings and pleasantries, he seemed ready to continue his narrative, but first asked whether I wanted to use the sleep mask again. He had placed it on the table in front of my chair.

"I imagine it could be helpful in 'visualizing' my blindness, if you'll forgive the mal a prop, but perhaps it made it a bit too vivid for you."

I said I'd make that decision as the story progressed, and sampled a few of Jackie's goodies.

"So the other day we were – that is, I was – on the road in Ohio. For the most part it was a two lane road, and traffic was light, so getting rides was harder than I expected, given the snow and wind and cold that should have given drivers a bit of sympathy for a man walking, even when I didn't have my thumb out.

"One fellow who did stop for me asked me where I was headed, and I had to think quickly, which I found a little difficult with a three-quarters frozen brain. 'West Coast,' I said, and he laughed out loud. He asked me a few more questions, and I imagine he looked me over pretty carefully, because I got the impression, as our conversation continued, that he thought I was crazy."

"What made you think so?" I asked.

"Well, a few things. I really wasn't dressed for the weather. I had only one pair of shoes, and those were loafers. They were soaked, and so were my socks, and even though I refrained from moaning and groaning, the car's heat was thawing them out, which was actually more than a little bit painful. I'd lost my hat a few days back when a gust of wind just blew it off my head, and even though I'd spent at least a good half hour walking around hoping to feel it with one of my frozen feet, I couldn't, so I gave up and went on with no protection for my brain either.

I shook my head, and was instantly glad Joe couldn't see that.

"Boy, you sure as hell didn't get an 'A+' in preparations for this trip, did you?" I asked.

I watched him smile, and felt a flash of amazement that we were sitting here in his near-castle of a home eating gourmet tidbits while he was telling me his story of the worst-planned pilgrimage in the history of mankind.

"No, Ron, I didn't plan the trip well, but you have to understand, I didn't feel as though I had too many choices. I had bills to pay, and I had a pretty sturdy attitude about people who don't pay their bills. I could have left one or two suppliers holding an empty bag and bought myself a decent coat and a pair of up-to-the-knee hiking boots, but that wasn't something I felt I could do, either then or today. As I've already mentioned, I didn't think I could stay home and be dependent on my family either. It just wasn't a choice. Whatever I was going to do, it had to be on my own."

"Yeah, OK, I get that, but seriously, three thousand miles in loafers, a short jacket and twenty-eight bucks in the middle of winter? It's still nuts!"

I watched him smile as he picked up a Greek olive and a bit of cheese, sniffing them before he popped them into his mouth.

"It was incredibly nuts, but it was what I could do at the time. And here we are today, neither of us with frozen feet or a single ketchup sandwich between us."

I had to shake my head at the truth of that.

"OK, OK, go on, Joe."

"You've been asking about my thoughts and feelings, Ron, and of course you can understand that they changed, often from minute to minute. On one hand, when I was crossing the Pennsylvania border into Ohio, I felt as though I had accomplished something, even though it was hard and I was uncomfortable, even miserable. On the other hand there were frustrations that made me question myself and my thinking.

"For instance, when someone would stop for me, I told you that I was careful not to reveal my blindness. That was mostly for my own safety, because of course I had no idea what kind of person was stopping for me, even though I was hugely grateful that they were doing so. I was especially careful if there were two or three people in the car, and even more so if they were all men. I had only a little money on me, as you know, but I really did want to hold onto what I had. However, with one or two exceptions everyone who picked me up turned out to be no problem..."

"—with one or two exceptions?" I asked.

"Right, and both were much later in the trip. What I was going to say, though, was that my efforts to keep my blindness to myself hampered me in other ways. Several times a driver would pull off the route that I was on to head for his own destination and I wouldn't notice it, so I wasn't able to say 'thank you, but I'll get out right here.' Because I didn't say that, he just continued on his own route. The result was I got taken off my route, and it took me sometimes hours, even a day to get back on the road I meant to stay on."

I started shaking my head again. The improbability of Joe's journey was rising to impossibility as it had earlier, and the idea that this man was just plain crazy was knocking on my brain. He had to be nuts, just looney tunes out of whack nuts...but...he wasn't. He was a clearly intelligent man, successful miles beyond his handicap, a wealthy man who certainly didn't get handed his wealth, a man who had found and married a beautiful and loving woman, who had children and grandchildren he was in love with, and so on. Hence the head-shaking.

Joe picked up a couple of cheese-covered crackers and chewed for a minute. I wondered whether he enjoyed telling his journey story, or whether it was painful to him. I suspected more the latter, which made me wonder why he would consent to drag up a thousand and one unpleasant memories just to tell it to a loser kid. I hate to think of myself as a kid, but compared to eighty-two, twenty-two is pretty much kid territory, and I've felt like a loser-kid pretty much of the time I'm not off inventing Facebook or Amazon, which is all the time.

"Anyway, where were we? I had begun suffering from another of my failures to plan. As I said, I was walking in loafers, which was tolerable on dry pavement or grass, became a real pain when it started snowing. Because the road I was (mostly) on was a rural two-lane, traffic was light, and got lighter with the snow, so walking became a greater part of my progress than I had hoped. When my shoes got wet, then full of snow, then froze, my feet froze too, and walking got harder. Whenever I came to a little town, I would feel my way along, looking for a service station with a bathroom. About half of them had a heat vent in the wall and I could take off my shoes and socks and thaw out my feet, then dry them off and put on a dry pair of socks. If no one else was waiting outside to use the men's room, I'd hold my wet shoes up against the heat vent to dry them out too, or at least warm them up. When I was feeling especially miserable, I resorted to a Hershey bar or a ketchup sandwich."

"Wasn't that frozen too?" I asked.

"No. Well, the Hershey bars were certainly cold, but I carried the ketchup bottle in my jacket pocket and the bread inside my jacket. It actually made the jacket feel a little warmer and left me one hand free to ward off poles and things in my path, and to stick my thumb out.

"I'd been on the road more than a week by this time, and in some ways I actually felt I was making progress. Not so much in terms of miles toward my destination, but in terms of learning to cope. My ability to concentrate on my senses, to listen for cars and even to identify the car by its engine sound, and to stay on my chosen road as I walked. Sleeping on billboard walkways on four of those nights and avoiding snake holes when I left the road shoulders, these were encouraging things. I worked pretty hard to stay focused on those thoughts, at least when I wasn't totally lost."

I started to shake my head again. "I can understand working to stay positive, but if it was me, I'm pretty sure I'd spend at least a few times shaking my fist at God. You know, like 'why me, God? What did I do to deserve this?' Didn't you ever go there?"

Joe stopped in mid-sip from his glass of wine. Putting the glass down, he wiped his mouth with a napkin and was silent for a minute.

"Ron, do you have a religion? A church?"

"Sure. Well, actually I'd have to say 'sorta kinda.' My parents are Catholic, but ever since I left home I'd have to admit I'm not into it much."

"I understand," he said, which was a relief. I thought for a second that I'd opened up a can of worms and he was going to give me a lecture about Sunday mass attendance and novenas and confessing my sins more often.

"I'm going to say something to answer your question, but I don't want you to take it as either a brag or a criticism of you, OK?"

I nodded, and then remembered for the thirtieth time that he couldn't see the nod. Duh! "Sure, OK," I said aloud.

"In all the time I was suffering emotionally from losing my sight," he said softly, "even before I made up my mind to leave Allentown and my family, and in all the time I was on the road and working on the west coast, I never once asked 'why me?'

"I never imagined that God had made me blind, or that blindness was any kind of punishment for sins that I may have committed. As to going blind, I just believe stuff happens -- to me, and to everyone. I believed then, and now, that God is with me and I am with Him before, during, and after it happens. If going blind happens to me, He is with me in suffering with it and in making the best of it, and making the best of it makes me a better man. I'm not saying I never felt sorry for myself. I suffered with fear that was close to paralyzing at times. But I never felt I'd been singled out for blindness, or that I'd been forsaken and abandoned by God, even though panic sometimes made me ask out loud where he was. In fact, he was with me every step of the way. He must have laughed at any number of my mistakes, but he was with me in suffering their consequences. And even in times when I was most miserable, I never compared my suffering with our Lord's suffering on the Cross."

Joe was silent then for several minutes, as if to let his own words echo in the room. As I listened to the echoes with him, I felt more than a little uncomfortable -- again. That was becoming a habit. His words were a declaration of his faith and his deepest values. In my discomfort I wanted to feel that they had tiptoed up to the edge of a lecture or a homily, but if I'm honest, they didn't get all the way there.

After that silence, all I could say was "I understand."

"OK then," he said, back into his journey. "Of all my memories, I have to say Ohio was ugly, as much because of my mistakes and strategies that didn't work out for me as because of the weather, but the weather did its best to make my teeth chatter, my toes fall off, and four-letter words escape my lips. I didn't often check my watch when I was walking, and I didn't want to have a driver who was giving me a ride see me pop my watch crystal to check the time with frozen fingers either, so I wasn't very good at sensing sunrise or sunset, except by the temperature, and that was by no means a reliable guide.

"When it was snowing, there were many times when I heard no traffic for as long as ten, fifteen, even twenty minutes or so. You know how falling snow muffles sound anyway, but I remember those times of snowy silence were times when I felt…well, I guess you could say kind of 'cosmically alone.' It was really profound silence, and more than once it made me imagine I was the last one on earth. In other circumstances it might have been beautiful, but for me it was mostly frightening. More than once I found myself praying as I walked, and kicking the snow under my feet, checking to see that I hadn't lost the road or gotten lost again."

I shuddered, just listening to Joe, right there in his toasty warm kitchen. It was fifty-six degrees and sunshine outside, probably a perfect seventy-two inside, but I was thinking of a nice hot bowl of soup.

"So you can imagine how grateful I was when I heard a car engine coming up from behind me, especially when its driver slowed down and stopped up ahead. Not every car had a heater worth the name in those days, but it was so good to get out of the snow and wind. I had to jump up and down a few times and kick the rocker panel to avoid getting too much snow into the driver's car, but as soon as I'd shut the door and he'd pulled out again, I must have said 'thank you!" about a dozen times.

"Several drivers said they were surprised to see someone walking in that weather, and even more someone who obviously hadn't dressed for it. I know those who asked thought I was seriously crazy, especially when I said I was heading for the other coast. I remember that there were a few pick-ups in which the driver was going my way for fifty, sixty, even a hundred miles or so, and felt like I'd hit a real jackpot."

I had no trouble imagining that feeling, and once again communicated my agreement by stupidly nodding my head before nearly smacking myself and saying (duh!) "I can imagine!"

"However…" Joe continued, ",,,those jackpots brought with them their own challenges, especially when the car's heater was working well. As I began to thaw out and get warm and cozy, my first reaction was to fall dead asleep. I think I was probably pretty thoroughly exhausted most minutes, hours, and days I was on the road, so sleep was both a blessing and a serious need."

"So what was the challenge?" I asked. "Still sounds like a jackpot to me!"

"Several of my pickups needed a companion – me -- to make conversation – to keep *them* awake, especially in the worst of the weather. I had to keep pinching myself and opening my window for a few breaths of *cold* air to keep my end of the talk going. On a couple of rides our conversation began to get pretty silly, but we had to keep it going if he was as tired as I was."

Joe's story was rapidly becoming a nightmare for me, almost difficult to imagine. I'd lived through a dozen or so winters of memory since I was nine or ten and started storing memories, and some of Joe's details were things I'd never remembered.

"Weren't the interstates being plowed?" I asked, again taking leave of my Swiss cheese education.

"Ron, Ron, remember your history books! The interstate system was built during Dwight Eisenhower's presidency. It began in January, 1953, but wasn't completed for years and years. This was December, 1954, and he didn't exactly ask Congress to fund the system on his first day in office. There were US highways, and several states had turnpikes, but no interstates."

"Oh. Yeah. Right. Sorry." I felt the wave of embarrassment wash over me, which was becoming way too familiar. Then I shook my head to clear the cobwebs and started to ask "OK, what happened next?" but I didn't. I found myself up to here with Joe's misery and my stupidity. I needed a break.

Chapter Eight

The Misery of Endurance – and the Endurance of Misery

As I lay on my bed I found it difficult…well no, impossible to think about anything except the long-running movie of Joe's journey, starring me. It was becoming a horror movie to end all horror movies. I hated it, for about a hundred reasons, but none of them stopped me from being utterly and completely fascinated by it.

I knew that Joe made at least a baker's dozen really poor decisions before he even *started* his journey, not the least of which was to start his journey at all. Walking across the country in winter while in summer loafers was one of the most incredible, but there were others, and here I was, imagining myself in his shoes.

I found myself needing, with increasing desperation, to find footholds, or finger holds, or even *fingernail* holds on the slippery cliffs of hope, or encouragement, or confidence as Joe (I) continued west toward Indianapolis. I had absolutely no imagination that I could put up with the misery and frustration that Joe had to be experiencing, what with hunger, cold, fears of wild animals, fears of getting lost two or twelve times a day, fears of waking up each morning as a six-foot frozen kielbasa, etc.

I felt beyond certain that I couldn't cope with what he had experienced, and it was still the first *third* of his trip, with two thousand and a few hundred more miles to go, and that's if he didn't get every hour or so. I would fail, sure as death and taxes.

On top of that, I was seriously choking on the really profound differences between Joe and me. I will be really honest here, at least for a minute. I don't have a whole lot of guilt about living off my Dad's salary. As far as I can see, he can afford me. Maybe not when he's sixty-six or seventy, but for the next several years he can feed me and even spot me a twenty or so when I want to hit a club or bar with the friends I don't have enough of.

Joe Cory, on the other hand, seems to have been born with a massive determination to achieve independence and live on his own earnings from what, kindergarten? Well, not exactly, but you catch my drift. I'd be a liar if I said I don't respect him for that.

These thoughts are filling my head as I lie here, and rather than enlightening, they make my head feel like it weighs a short ton or two.

Still, as I wrestle with all of this, I recognize that even the sour stew of misery and fear and frustration that Joe must have been feeling as he trudged west, there were times when he must have felt like he was getting used to it, surviving, and even making progress. The surviving part was probably a real source of encouragement, like "OK, life is shittier than shit right now, but I'm dealing with it, and I'm further west than I was yesterday."

Finally, when I get really grim thinking about all this stuff, I remind myself that the only alternatives in front of Joe are death by surrender -- and death by suicide. For Joe, surrender to a life of dependence on his father and older brothers was just not tolerable, and so was entirely off the table. I realized that I didn't really feel the same, at least for a while. Eventually I know I'm going to have to steer my own boat, however poorly that might be.

As to suicide, I figure I'm enough of a loser right now without becoming a total loser by taking a Swiss Army knife to my wrists.

Anyway, I'm going to sleep now. I need rest if I'm going back to co-star in any further westward miseries.

Chapter Nine
Turn Left – Or Die

Three days later I was actually excited to visit with Joe and hear more of his journey. It occurred to me, in a fit of brilliance, that if he was going to be sitting with me in the comfort of his pretty magnificent home telling me his story, its outcome wasn't exactly a mystery, and no matter how bad the conditions he was yet to face, I could pretty much guess that he faced them and survived. That piece of profound insight on my part helped me actually look forward to hearing more.

Once again, Jackie plied us with nibble-goodies, and retreated to a distant part of their apartment. The entertainment was sometimes difficult, but the concessions in this theater of the mind were outstanding.

"So, where did we leave off?" Joe asked.

"I think you were opening the passenger window to steal some cold air to keep you awake while you kept your latest driver awake…"

"Right, right," he said.

"OK, Indiana was encouraging for me, at least at first. The land was flatter, even in snow, so walking was a little easier, and it was my third state, so I was beginning to feel that while I was miserable, I was surviving, so it didn't seem quite as frightening.

"Even at night, when you had to leave the road to try to find a billboard to sleep on?" I asked.

"Well remember, Ron, being blind, the only way I knew night from day was by snapping off the crystal of my watch and feeling the hands very gently, which I only did while in someone's car. A couple of times I had let it slip that I was blind, so I could ask whether it was am or pm, and then try to hold onto that like a touchpoint for the following day or two.

"I think there were only three rides between the Indiana border and the outskirts of Indianapolis, and the last one was with a man who was able to take me 40 or 50 miles west, which was great, because it started snowing again and the roads were getting a good bit worse. It was a huge relief to get warm, and as we talked, I learned he was heading to Springfield, Illinois, which was a piece of real good fortune, because I could stay warm for a good long time.

"However, good news has a way of disappearing in a flash, and it did as we approached Indianapolis. I noticed that he was driving more and more slowly, and a few times he seemed to slide and fishtail a bit. It was already snowing pretty hard when he picked me up, but now it was getting really difficult for drivers.

"When we got into the outskirts of the city, he had to stop altogether. Hand-made signs and wooden barricades told him the road west was closed. He told me he'd have to find a motel or cabin and spend the night there. I put my shoes back on and my jacket, and asked him to drop me there, so that I didn't get lost.

Once I was out walking again, it didn't take me long to decide getting out wasn't the best idea I'd had. The snow was up half way to my knees on the roadside, and even though the road itself had been plowed earlier, its surface was now over the tops of my shoes. I remember wishing that I hadn't lost my hat a week or so earlier. I really missed it."

"I walked with one foot in the deep snow only for a really short time – that proved impossible, but I was afraid to walk with both feet on the plowed surface because even with light traffic, I'd just experienced how slippery it was. The snow was so heavy it muffled the sounds of what traffic there was, and I strained to hear every sound coming from behind me, ready to jump into the deep snow if I had to, even though the plows that had already come through had built that snow up really high.

"Thankfully, it wasn't long before I came to an intersection where I could hear occasional vehicles coming from my left and right. A truck pulled up behind me and the driver honked twice. I looked up in his direction and he honked again. I called out "can you help me?" He yanked the passenger door open and said "get in!" I had to climb up to do that and slipped once, but got in and thanked him. He asked what I was doing out on the road alone in this weather, and when I told him I was heading west, he laughed and told me how crazy I was and that I wasn't going to be able to go further that night. I asked him if he could drop me at an open service station, and happily he did just that, a few hundred yards ahead.

"That station was about to close. I went into its little office area and explained to the owner that I was alone on the road and needed a place to stay for the night. He thought I was asking for a hotel, and started to recommend one, but I had to tell him no, because I don't have money for a hotel, and asked if I could stay in his rest room. He started to say "no," but when he looked me over and saw that I was already soaked from the knees down and my head was dripping with snow too, he relented, but asked for identification and said that if he found any damage in the morning he'd have me arrested."

I started getting exhausted again as the horror movie frames ran through my head, even as I reached for another handful of peanuts and a sip of Prosecco.

"Joe," I said. "You're killing me here. You were just talking a few minutes ago about feeling all encouraged and puffed up because you'd made it to Indiana, and now this. Yuck!"

Joe smiled. "Well yeah, that was a tough stretch, but I did get to stay out of the weather that night and his men's room was cleaner than most and I didn't have to try to huddle on my suitcase to stay out of the wind, so the next morning (and I knew it was morning from snow plows going past and traffic starting, even before the owner arrived to start the day) I felt better than I could possibly have felt if I'd had to pass the night outside, right?"

I shook my head. "Oh sure, and the station owner brought you Egg Mc Muffins and hash browns for breakfast, right? Sheesh!"

Joe laughed out loud, and so did I.

"No, no muffins (no McDonalds yet either,) but when he got in, and I told him I was blind, he gave me good clear walking directions to Route 13, about a mile from the station. Route 13 wasn't going to get me any further west, but I was going to take it anyway. I had decided it was a good time for a switch in strategy. I was going to head south, and see how fast I could get out of the cold and snow."

"My God!" I said. "Signs of brain function! Congratulations!"

Joe laughed out loud, and I was suddenly both embarrassed at my own rudeness and grateful for his good humor.

"Not so fast!" he said. "Turning south was not the end of my misery or my fears. Not by a long shot. As a matter of fact, I'd have to say that my demons only changed shape, and my road course became a good deal more confused."

("Damn!") I had become so enmeshed in Joe's physical and emotional miseries that I really, really didn't want to hear that. It was time for another break – for me anyway.

Chapter Ten
Cold – To the Bone

"Deep snow had been really hard to walk in, making my way through Indiana, and trying to find shelter at night when there were no service station restrooms to use was no picnic. But turning south was a decision forced on me, not by my difficulties, but by the westward roads in front of me being closed. Remember there were no Interstate highways then, and road plowing was a poor shadow of what it is today.

"In hindsight, it was probably a good, even necessary thing, because if I'd stayed on my original route I'd have had to walk and hitch through Kansas or Nebraska, and on into Colorado, where I would have had to cross the Rocky Mountains in January, and I don't have much imagination about how I'd have been able to do that…certainly not on foot.

"Still, turning south was not the end of my challenges."

I was listening hard for signs of encouragement, and was immediately disappointed when Joe said that. I'd been more drawn into Joe's story than I'd ever imagined possible, so much so that I felt more of his miseries and fears than I even wanted to…every bit of me felt as if I was walking with him, and much of the time I felt as blind as he was, sleep mask or not.

The day before I sat down with him for our next slog of his story, I'd been home relaxing when I got a surprise visit from my grandfather, who of course wanted to know how my visits with Joe were going.

I told him how stone crazy I thought the old man was for even attempting to get across the country on his own, and how my judgement about his craziness only grew deeper as I "descended" into his trip with him. I also admitted that I was way more wrapped up in the progress of his story than I could have imagined before it started.

"So OK, then, what do you think of the man now?" my Grandfather asked. It took me several minutes to even start to answer him.

"I think…well, I think he's nothing like me and I'm nothing like him, for one thing…

"…and his situation was way different from mine when he made up his mind to take off on his trip…."

"Really? What is it you think was so different?"

"Shit, Grandpa, he lost his entire sight at age 19, like he was suddenly and totally disabled, and he'd been running his own business and he'd even enlisted in the Air Force already, and everything. Even though he was four years younger than I am now, he was a good bit past where I am. I haven't done much of anything, and I have no real ideas about what to do or where to go."

He just looked at me like he was trying to figure out what planet I'd come from. Probably Melmac.

"Anything else?" he asked.

"Well, he'd been brought up in a family where everybody worked, from like birth...or childhood anyway. Things were different then. People who were poor lived without a lot of the things we have, so I guess they looked at work differently too. Listening to Joe, I'd say that in his mind, there was no such thing as a bad job. Any job that paid anything was worth having. His family didn't even have television or central heat in their house!"

Grandpa just sat there listening and looking at me in that weird, vaguely insulting way. Then he just stood up and said "OK, then. You going to keep visiting with him and hear the rest of his story?"

"Yeah. I mean I gotta say I'm hooked on his story, looney tunes as it is. The man had genuine cujones, sure as shit!"

As he turned to leave, he stopped and looked over his shoulder. "One day, hopefully sooner than later, Ron Brantley, you're going to learn to express yourself like a grown-up who knows words longer than four letters...sure as shit!"

I was still red-faced when he went out the door. It occurred to me that "empathy" has more than four letters, but Grandpa didn't seem to have much of that for me. I started feeling sorry for myself, which is something I'd been doing a lot lately, but that brought me back to Joe.

Joe Cory had more reason to feel sorry for himself than I've ever had, yet in all his conversation so far, I hadn't noticed even a whiff of that, at least after he decided he wasn't going to jump off a bridge (I didn't know if they even *have* bridges or rivers in Allentown, Pennsylvania, but that's beside the point.)

Joe just seems like a man who believes we are born with a purpose. Not necessarily a "calling" or some specific career we're supposed to fall into, but a more general purpose – maybe just the purpose to support one's self and a few others by one's work. It seems to me he never questioned that belief, even when he was a little kid, kind of like it was baked into his protoplasm.

Ah hah! And therein lies my problem, I thought. I'm only half baked. It almost made me laugh, though I really didn't think it was too funny. I was suddenly anxious to see Joe again. I had questions.

Mrs. Joe was her sweet self, as usual. She must have thought that men tend to get into trouble if they aren't eating something. It was OK, though. Her stuff was always good to eat, and because I ate about three quarters of what she put out, it meant I was listening instead of talking. We sat again on opposite sides of Joe's kitchen table.

"Let's see. Where were we?" he began. "I think I was saying that turning south was not by any means the end of frozen feet and hard walking. First of all, the snow didn't stop at the Indianapolis city limits. But Route 13 was open, and one driver who knew the state suggested that route, southwest through Bloomington and into Kentucky west of Louisville. Between my frozen feet and my right thumb, I worked hard to keep moving. I think the snow lasted for another day or so, and it was two, probably two and a half days when I crossed the Indiana border. That's when it turned to rain. But it wasn't just rain, it was cold rain and colder wind, and the clothes I had were soaked in minutes, where before I could brush the snow off my jacket every mile or so. I had to walk as hard as I could just to generate enough body heat to keep going. If I'd stood still I think I would have shivered to death."

I swallowed my chewy bite of apricot paste and raised a hand to stop him, but of course it didn't... until I spoke up.

"Joe, hold on a minute. I need to ask some questions – about things that have been on my mind for a few days now. Is that OK?"

He smiled and nodded. "Sure, Ron, stop me anytime!"

"OK, here goes. As I've listened to your story so far, I've gotten the sense that there are some real and serious differences between us."

"Oh? What differences are you seeing?"

"Well, I guess one is that you grew up, from a small boy, with the belief that relying on yourself was like, totally important, and being dependent on someone else was sort of – how do I put this? – kind of 'cosmically wrong.' Am I right?"

Joe was silent for a long time and even his silence felt oddly encouraging, as if I'd sparked a serious sidebar.

"That's a good question, Ron. I'm not sure that was a belief that I had actually declared. It wasn't a 'philosophy' that I held consciously, but even though I'd never articulated it, I would have to say that yes, I believed it. Why do you ask?"

"Well, I guess I would have to say I have neither believed it nor articulated it in my own life, but I also haven't been very comfortable in my own skin being dependent – on my parents, for example. I guess my question really is, like 'where is it written' that all of us are supposed to be on our own and self-supporting and all of that? Where was it written for you?"

Again, Joe took his time coming up with his words, and somehow I took a small compliment from the time he took to think before he answered.

"Let me put it this way. From my early childhood, I have remembered how my parents lived their lives. My mother would always be the first to get up in the morning to attack a set of chores that were hers to do, from lighting the kitchen fire to warm the house, to making breakfast, making the lunch I carried to school and my father ate on the job, doing laundry, cleaning the house, baking communion wafers for our church, and a hundred other things. I don't remember anyone telling her to do those things. She just accepted that it was her responsibility. My father dressed, shaved, combed his hair, came down to breakfast, then went out get the trolley to his job as a chippier at Bethlehem Steel. He worked eight to twelve hours every day, six days a week, in good weather and bad. Sundays were for mass and reading his Bible, while my mother made Sunday dinner. I had chores to do around the house, cutting the grass, helping my father, doing the dishes after supper, later with my paper routes, and so on. My brothers and sister had their own chores as well. None of us knew any different. We all did what we did and none of us children had any choice about it.

"Our family did as well as it did only because everyone contributed. I knew other children, ones from wealthy families in school who lived very differently, and once or twice I envied them, playing baseball or football and just doing nothing on long summer afternoons, but that was not a choice I was given."

"But Joe," I asked. "What I really want to know is, how did you feel about that? You said you envied the rich kids. Did you feel like you got short-changed?"

Again, he hesitated, and again I felt like I was on a roll, getting into things that were important – at least to me.

"I'm sure there were a few times when I'd have preferred to have fewer chores, fewer jobs, and more time to play or do nothing, but several factors made those moments few and far between."

"What factors were those?

"Well, for one thing, I was the baby in the family. My parents never questioned the need to do the work they did, day in and day out. My brothers and sisters had their own chores, and then their own jobs to do. I was never asked to do anything that they weren't already doing. And both my mother and father paid close attention to the way I handled my responsibilities. When I did a good job, there was a nickel for an ice cream cone, and they were generous with their compliments, but when I took shortcuts, they let me know about it then, too."

"Did you get punished when you slacked off?"

"I don't remember getting physically punished at all, because slacking off wasn't a habit or a choice I had. It wasn't permitted to my brothers, and not to me. If I decided I wanted to play instead of delivering my papers, my customers wouldn't be able to read the news, and the paper would give my route to someone else. I knew there were consequences for not doing my work and rewards for doing it well."

"Rewards? Like what?"

Joe almost laughed. "Rewards like getting a second paper route, like getting more customers in my service station, like making a few more dollars and being able to take a girl out to a movie. And knowing that my parents were proud of me. Believe it or not, that was something very important to me, from a very young age…although…"

"Although?" I asked.

"Although I don't mean to paint a picture of myself as a model boy scout or saint of some kind. Earlier on, I did have objections to some of the limits on fun and games with other kids, and in fact I actually 'ran away' four or five times when I was frustrated or angry. I never got very far on those little 'escape' trips, and my parents were pretty confident that after an hour or so they could find me ten or twelve blocks away."

As I listened, felt like I was being dragged, almost kicking and screaming, despite the fact that Joe Cory was one of the gentlest of men I've ever met. I really didn't want to be wrong about this, but I felt like I was at the edge of a yawning reality toward which I was being dragged. It felt like a cliff and there were spear points buried in the ground a few thousand feet down. I suddenly didn't want to hear any more of Joe's answer to my question…but he wasn't finished.

"Ron, how old are you again?"

"Uh, twenty-two."

"OK, let's pretend that your father decides tomorrow to quit his job…and your mom too."

"Why would they do that? They're happy doing what they do!"

"That's something for you to think about, but just go with me for a moment. They both decide they've had enough of getting up each morning and going off to work. They decide that there is enough money in their retirement fund to feed and house the two of them, but not their children."

(Groan!) "OK, so I'd be up shit's creek. So what?"

"Well, let's expand the thought. Suppose all parents of their generation come to the same decision one day this month. What happens then?"

(Sigh…) "Well, that's no longer shit's creek. It's the freakin' Mississippi shit river!"

Joe actually laughed.

"OK," he said, "let's come back a step. Let's assume for a minute that everyone in your parents' generation actually decides to forgive you and everyone else in your generation for not wanting to fend for yourselves, and they go on supporting you until they die."

"Well, OK. It's not about to happen, but OK."

"But suppose the members of your generation, all of them dependent on their parents' generosity, decide to fall in love, or just have sex, and create a new generation. Let's say each of your millennial brothers and sisters makes a couple of children. Given their parents' example, what's going to be

75

their attitude toward personal responsibility and financial independence?"

There was silence in the room, and Joe let it drag on. As for me, I developed a really strong desire to be somewhere else. Anywhere else.

"Can we get back to your trip across the country?"

Joe smiled, and I only exhaled when he said "sure, but think about that, OK?"

Chapter Eleven
The Confidence of Insanity

Joe launched into his story again, and I was glad to get back into it. Sure enough, it didn't take long for me to get wrapped up in even the small details of his lunatic journey. In more than one way it reminded me of my Middle School reading of Gulliver's Travels, not because the people he met on his journey were aliens, but because the trip itself was, for me, a totally alien adventure.

"So, where were we? Oh yes, on that two-lane route heading south. A little past Bloomington, the snow finally tapered off, or I should say it got enough warmer to turn to sleet, and then rain. It was still probably about thirty-eight or forty degrees. That's when I began feeling more miserable then ever – when I was getting soaked and frozen at the same time."

"Damn, Joe! I was looking forward to the end of misery, and now it's worse?"

"It was, Ron. But even though the weather was worse on my body, and in between bouts of fear whenever I got myself totally lost away from any road, my confidence was growing in other ways."

"Like what?" I asked. I could barely imagine his misery, let alone an *increase*(!!) in his confidence.

"Well," he said, "for one thing, I was growing familiar with my considerably heightened senses of hearing, touch, even smell, and with my ability to concentrate, which heightened those senses even more. Even when I was trying to disguise my blindness, I'd make conversation with the men who picked me up, asking questions to confirm that I'd just recognized a car passing by us by its engine sound alone. I was using another skill that had begun with my loss of sight, echo-location, which gave me surprisingly accurate perception of where sounds were coming from, how close they were, and whether they were approaching or fading away.

"Once the snow stopped, I was again enjoying the improved sense of touch in my feet. I could tell where the edge of the road was, where the shoulder stopped, and what the ground was like further off the road. I could make steadier progress with one foot on the tarmac and one on the gravelly shoulder, even though being cold and wet made me even more miserable."

"Well," I said, "I guess some clouds have silver linings, don't they? But what did these hearing and touch skills actually do for you? I mean, how did they help you get closer to the coast?"

"Good question, and here's an example. A fellow stopped for me in a pick-up truck just after I'd crossed from Kentucky into western Tennessee. I think that was the first totally dry day I'd experienced since western Ohio. He asked me where I was going and I told him I was heading for the west coast. He laughed, and we talked for a bit about the miseries I'd been suffering, but then he said he was going in my direction for about a hundred and twenty-five miles, but he had to stop in a few minutes and pick up a car he was going to tow further west. I didn't think anything about that, and he got to a farm along the road and hitched the car to his pick-up. What surprised me was a second stop he made a few miles further on. There he took responsibility for a third vehicle, a Pontiac sedan, and asked me if I would drive the Pontiac and follow him and his pickup to a spot about a hundred miles further west."

"And you said 'no' of course. I'm guessing you'd been masquerading successfully as a man with eyes, right?"

"Well, I guess I had been, but no, I didn't turn *him* down."

"What!?"

"Remember, Ron, when we talked about a kind of 'sonar' that I'd begun using when I left Allentown? By this time on my trip, I'd developed my echolocation skills quite a bit. I had learned to recognize *what* was making each sound, and not only *what* is was, but where it was coming from, whether it was approaching or getting further away. I'd learned to estimate its speed as well. The more I relied on echolocation, the more acute my hearing became, and the faster I was able to process the data I was picking up, probably because I was just paying so much more attention than ever before to sounds, or even the absence of sounds my ears were picking up. Whatever synapses of my brain were engaged in echolocation, they enabled me to achieve something very close to 'sight.' If it helps you to understand, imagine a baby. It hears things, gets data through its ears, but it needs intellect to interpret the data and draw meaning from it. That only comes as the baby grows and matures. In my case, I'd had nineteen years in which I'd learned to associate sight with sounds to interpret what was going on around me, and I'd learned enough to make useful sense of what I was now receiving only through my ears.

"You asked me to give you an example of my confidence in echolocation and in my other senses. Once I got behind the wheel of the Pontiac and turned the key, I opened all four windows. As I expected, I could use my hearing and echolocation to recognize the sound of his truck and how close I was to it, and in what direction it was moving. I told him to start out slowly at first, explaining that I wanted to get the "feel" of the car, but what I was really wanting was to get the feel of my ability to follow him accurately. Turned out I was able to do quite well as long as a bunch of traffic didn't get between my Pontiac and his Ford pick-up. Happily, the road we were on was a two-lane, and there wasn't much traffic and almost no room for other drivers to get between us. I made it the whole way without getting lost and with no dents on either the Pontiac or the towed vehicle."

"Yeah, sure."

"Seriously. I'm not exaggerating and I'm surely not lying, Ron."

"Yeah, I understand, and your explanation of echolocation does make a kind of sense, but still; you drove a car 100 miles, totally blind. No accidents, no dents. That's still whacko in my brain. Maybe I don't have enough intellect to process it!"

"That could be, but every word I just said is true, Ron."

"No shit?"

"No shit."

"Holy crap!"

"How about just 'oh my goodness' or something more like that?" Joe smiled.

"Right. Sorry." I remembered my Grandfather's admonition about my language, and my cheeks turned a little pinker than usual.

"Actually," he continued, "there was one detail that I wish hadn't been true. With all four windows open, even at somewhere around thirty or thirty-five miles an hour, it was colder than – well, really cold! And while the Pontiac had heat, I had to keep the blower down to minimum speed so I could concentrate on hearing the sounds of the pick-up truck in front of me and which way it was heading. I could have used more heat!"

"Oh, poor baby!" I said. "But I mean still, that's quite a story, and I hope you don't mind if I say I think you were crazy to even try it."

I could feel he was proud of himself, not just for having completed this feat, but even for just telling someone about it.

"Well, I suppose I can admit to a kind of fearlessness in it, but I don't think I'm stupid now and I wasn't stupid then either. I wouldn't have agreed to drive the car if I didn't think I could do it. I knew I could use echolocation at a walking pace, so my only concern was whether I could do it at 25 to 35 miles per hour. It turned out I could, and I did.

"I'll bet you did!" I said.

"Anyhow, we got to his destination, dropped off the towed car and the Pontiac and headed back out on the road, which ended up being not exactly advantageous to my objectives."

"Really?" I asked. "How so?"

"Well, when I got out of the snow, as I've said, it was still really cold, and often wet with rain that soaked my clothes and quickly made me more miserable than the snow had. You can understand that I was more grateful than ever when someone picked me up.

"And that worked against you how?"

"I'm sure you can imagine that when I got into someone's car, out of the rain and into the warmth, I wasn't exactly anxious to tell the driver to stop and let me out every time he made a turn that even felt like it was a little bit off my route…or what I thought my route should be, which often changed.

"As a result, my progress toward the west coast became a lot more wandering. I was hoping to hit Memphis and the Mississippi within a couple of days of turning south in Indianapolis, but with cold and rain I found myself passing through Nashville, Knoxville, and even a little bit of Northwest Georgia before I got turned around and heading more or less due west."

I was still in a funny kind of taunting mood after Joe's driving story. So I asked: "Well, you could have just volunteered to take over the wheel and take the direct route, right?"

"No, there were no more driving spells for me all the way across the country, Ron."

"OK, sorry if that was offensive."

"It's not a problem."

"So how long DID it take you to get to the Mississippi?"

"Well, I have to think…I would say I was a week or more wandering around the south…probably more. But at least there was no more snow, and thank God, it didn't rain every day. If the temperature was in the 40s, I could walk more easily, especially in dry shoes and jacket."

"Did you find more service station bathrooms than billboards for sleeping?"

"Some of each. One night, sleeping on a billboard walkway, was worse for me than all the others. Somewhere in the middle of the night, I was awakened suddenly by a really sharp pain in my left thigh. I had no idea what it was at first, but suddenly I realized it was an insect and it was biting me. I immediately imagined a poisonous spider like a brown recluse and jumped up and dropped my trousers. I found the spider still attached to my leg and smashed it in a fit of panic. When I had caught my breath and gotten myself back together lying on my suitcase, I was still in serious pain. When I woke up the next morning, my whole leg was swollen, down to my foot, so much so that I couldn't get my shoe on. I had to crush the heel and wear the shoe like a slipper for several days. The pain kept throbbing and I was afraid things were going to get worse, perhaps even to the extent of killing me."

I shivered violently just thinking about brown recluse spiders.

"What made me most afraid was that at the same time I was suffering with the spider bite, I was becoming short of breath, wheezing and coughing, and even running a pretty good fever. I imagined that all my symptoms were related to the bite, though in hindsight I've decided that it was a coincidence, and I'd just come down with a bad cold or even pneumonia."

"Couldn't you get yourself to a doctor?" Even being without money, I couldn't imagine a local family doc refusing to help him without cash in hand.

"I thought about it, but I wasn't very confident about asking for help. I was in the deep South, and I hadn't found quite the same level of kindness and greetings in Georgia and Alabama or even Mississippi and Louisiana as I had up north. And of course I couldn't have paid any doctor for seeing me, so I didn't ask."

"Really? How long were you sick?"

He thought for a couple of minutes. "I'd say the swelling in my leg lasted at least a week before I could get my shoe back on properly, and my coughing and wheezing took a couple of weeks to become a memory. That period was probably my lowest of the whole trip."

"I'll bet!"

"Well, listening to me telling my story, Ron, you can tell, I'm sure, that I'm not a southern boy. Folks in those states could tell that too, as soon as I opened my mouth. I just felt what southern folks felt – a little sense of 'distance' between us, and perhaps even a little uneasiness about the perceived distance. Of course my blindness also made me different, and hitch-hiking across the country as a blind man was something people didn't encounter every day. I had the sense that nobody was very comfortable with me. Only one or two service station managers put me out into the rain overnight, but even the rest didn't overwhelm me with 'southern hospitality.'

"Still, Joe, you've said that you were gaining confidence as your trip progressed. Isn't that true?"

"It was, and I was extremely grateful for that. But another part of me harbored fears and frights that were as vivid and even paralyzing as for any young child. One of those was snakes. I'd been afraid of copperheads and the occasional rattlesnakes in the northeast, but now that I was in the South I was even more frightened of water moccasins and other snakes that made nights sleeping outside really difficult for me. My newly acute hearing was often imagining the softest rustle somewhere a few feet away as a hungry cottonmouth coming toward my scent. I'm not sure how many minutes and hours I spent frozen in fear.

"There was one frigid and rainy night in Louisiana, on a country road outside Opelousas, in really swampy country, where I got dropped off by a driver who was turning back east. I really didn't want to get out, but I'd been wandering too much, so I did. I asked him if he knew of any place I could stay for the night. He said there were some cabins just down the road we were on, maybe a mile or two ahead. I told him I was blind, and that surprised him. He said there wasn't much of a sign anyway, and he thought he remembered it had a gravel driveway.

"I started walking in my usual way, with one foot on the pavement and one on the shoulder, and there was not a single piece of traffic anyway, but I was deathly afraid of taking even one step off the asphalt, and of slipping into the swamp that was right there beside the road. I heard various splashes and animal noises with almost every step. With the rain, I was soaked to the skin in a couple of minutes. When I did finally find the place, I walked up the driveway to what I hoped was the proprietor's office and knocked on the door. It wasn't the office, but the second one was, thank God, and I explained that I was blind and walking to the West Coast. I told him I had very little money, but could I please get out of the rain and spend the night in one of his cabins. He said he never got business in December or January anyway, and he agreed to let me stay one night for a dollar. He pointed me to the right and said "first door you come to."

"When I got to the cabin, felt for the door and went in, I found a wooden bed with a straw mattress, a single blanket and a fireplace, which I didn't bother to light. I pulled off my wet clothes and laid them across two chairs and a table and put on all the dry clothes I had with me. Three or four times I stopped, rigid with fear, at the sound of something rustling near me in the cabin. I would have been grateful if it was just a rat or mouse, but when I lay down on the bed, I don't think I slept a wink, listening for even softer rustlings of snakes. I'm sure it was the most frightened I've ever been in my life."

I actually shivered.

"You know," I said, "it occurs to me that long before this point in your trip, you must have been totally exhausted. I mean if I'm you, I'm not exactly getting my customary eight hours of snooze – on any night! I'm listening for every damn rustle in the bushes. I'm freezing my butt off, and I'm guessing it's what – three or four weeks since I've been on a mattress with a pillow and decent bed covers. I'm thinking my back would be killing me, my neck would be stiffer than a board, and I'd be muttering curses even *I* think are bad!"

One of the things I most enjoy while sitting with Joe listening to his story is that when I say things like that, he seems to enjoy my comments. I actually make the man laugh now and then, and I have to say I find that really generous on his part. I'm starting to feel like we're becoming friends. This moment was one of those, and after his laugh, he stopped and thought for a minute or two.

"You know, Ron, you're probably more right than wrong. I certainly didn't enjoy a lot of the things I had to go through. I'd have been grateful to have avoided the physical miseries and my fear of animals, especially snakes, and I'm sure I was truly, even profoundly exhausted.

"But at the same time it felt like a genuine adventure, and I was really encouraged by what I was learning, and the ways I was developing my ability to concentrate and let my other senses make up for a good bit of what I couldn't see. By the time I woke up after that terrible night in Louisiana, and got on the road again, I just felt glad to be out of there, and the distance I'd already come seemed like something of an achievement."

"You've mentioned that a couple of times...is that how you were able to keep your spirits up after all the miseries?

"I'd have to say 'yes' and 'not so much.' I'd been stopping in stores several times to buy my white bread and ketchup, and each purchase lasted me only about three or four days. So by Texas, I was beginning to run out of my $28 'grub-stake' pretty fast, and I still had a long way to go.

"On the happy side, I was happy to get past the Louisiana swamps and the temperatures were a good bit warmer and drier. They weren't exactly 'warm' but they weren't freezing either. The land was a lot flatter too, so that was great, but I'd been imagining that I could get across Texas on one long road, like Route 66 or something like that. No such luck. The country roads zig-zagged from one state-numbered route to another which made crossing the state much longer...

"...so walking was finally a lot easier, but it seemed there was more of it to do. Also, because traffic was really light I didn't get picked up as often. And one other thing: even though I was near the peak of my listening and concentrating powers, there was very little reward for my sensory strengths. It was just really, really quiet – and I wasn't used to that at all. Looking back on that stretch now, I remember feeling it was almost spooky.

Also, I found myself getting hungrier, both because I was trying to make my money last, and because there weren't many places along my roads to buy anything. I think I went two or three days with nothing to eat at least twice, maybe three times, in Texas, and maybe three more times on the rest of my trip.

Compulsively, I reached for one of Mrs. Cory's cookies to calm my imagination.

"When I did get picked up, I was grateful as usual, and one time I got something to eat besides ketchup sandwiches. One fellow who picked me up took me about 40 miles and then pulled off the road at a diner to get himself a late breakfast. I went in with him to carry on our conversation. He ordered eggs, bacon, sausage, and biscuits and they came with a bowl of grits. He asked why I didn't order anything. I told him I just wasn't hungry, which was probably the biggest lie I've ever told. I didn't want to ask for charity, but when he was finished eating, he hadn't touched his grits…said he didn't like them, but asked if I wanted them. (I think he was suspecting my 'not hungry' lie.) I said "Oh, OK," trying hard not to show my enthusiasm, and I have to tell you, they were delicious!"

Once again I was amazed, actually more than amazed, at least partly because I couldn't imagine holding so tightly to a set of morals that made Joe refuse to ask for help – or "charity" – as he called it. I sensed that it was some kind of tortured pride, though maybe there was more to it than that. I thought about all the times I'd asked my Mom and Dad for a little extra help. I always got it, often even more than I'd even asked for, so I couldn't understand why it was so hard for Joe.

I was wrestling with that question when Joe suggested stopping there and carrying on the next day. On my way out I grabbed another cookie to quiet my psychosomatic hunger.

Chapter Twelve

"Snakes!!"

We were seated on Joe's back patio for a change, and Jackie actually handed us a cold beer from the local brewery. Then came a platter of slices sausages and chips – my kind of party!

"So!" I said. "On to Texas!"

"And New Mexico, Arizona, and finally the Promised Land!" he said with a smile.

."Were you still 'bill-boarding' at night? I asked -- And still believing that snakes don't climb?"

"Not so much," he said, "and don't go wrecking my child-like snake beliefs! I had enough fears!

"No, not so many billboards," he continued, "but have you seen those old-fashioned country gas station/general store buildings with a roof extending out across the front and covering the one-or-two gas pumps, so people could fill up out of the rain?"

I have seen them, and actually I think they're kind of romantic. I once imagined buying one for a song in some broken down country town and fixing it up into a kind of six-table restaurant and variety store. Of course my fantasy involved such monster success that I franchised it and became Donald Trump's rich cousin. I've admitted that I'm not exactly a portrait of drive and ambition these days, but I can dream, can't I?

Anyway, Joe described climbing the two or three steps leading up to the store's front door and just sacking out on the top step for the night. It kept him dry anyway, and he managed to be gone before the store opened up the next day, even when the owner lived in the small apartment on the upper floor.

"Sometimes," he said, "there was no gas station/store, so I waited until my watch told me most people who lived along the road had turned out their lights and gone to sleep. I'd curl up on their front porch, and then wake myself up early enough, when the birds started chirping, to move on before I was discovered. It worked out pretty well, especially because the weather had dried out and I could cope with the cold much better when I wasn't wet."

"You had learned to carry water with you every day, right?"

Joe smiled his gentle smile, and once again I was impressed with his refusal to take offense at my jibes.

"I had, and most of the time I had no trouble refilling my water jug. But I remember asking one storekeeper if he would refill my jug for me. He took it and went to a sink at the back of his store. When he'd filled it and put it down on the counter, he said 'that'll be twenty-five cents.' I told him I couldn't afford that, and he could empty it again. He must have shaken his head or something I couldn't see, but he said he wouldn't do that. "That'd be a damn waste of good water, son, and we don't get a lot of that around here."

"I reached for the jug and he snatched it back out of my reach. He said: "Another move like that and the price will go up to fifty-cent!"

I wished I could reach across the counter and smack him, but thought better about that. I lowered my voice and explained to him that I was blind, and trying really hard to hitch-hike across the country from Pennsylvania, and I could really use his help and kindness. "If it'll make any difference I'll buy a loaf of white bread and a bottle of ketchup.

"He just said 'shee-it!" and walked around behind me to fetch the bread and ketchup. When he came back behind the counter, he said "That'll be fifty-three cents, water included." It was a high price, but I walked out with new food and a full jug."

"Where was this?" I asked.

"Nowhere, Texas," he said. "I didn't pass through any of the big cities like Houston or Dallas or even Austin. I got pretty close to El Paso as I was about to leave the state behind, but that was several days later."

I took a pull on my beer. Thinking about being Joe, and being thirsty and hungry for days at a time, as well as putting up with dipsticks like the gas station guy made both the beer and the sausages taste absolutely delicious. It also made Joe seem like a genuine man among men, and made me feel like a marshmallow. As that thought smacked me upside the head, I suddenly felt very tired.

"Joe, I need to ask you an off-the-subject question. It doesn't have anything to do with your journey, but maybe you can help me with something."

"Sure, Ron! What's on your mind?"

"I think I've kind of brought this up before, but it keeps coming up in my head. Why do you think you were able to

92

embark on this journey, all alone, totally blind, only $28 in your pocket, and make it to the other end of the continent and carry on until you're sitting here 80-something years old in a house big enough for every dream I've ever had, while I'm exhausted by the mere thought of going out and getting a job at McDonalds? Are we really from different planets?"

It was kind of funny just then. I watched Joe's face and he did his hesitation ('that's a big question and I have to think about it...') thing, but I half suspected he'd been waiting for the question and had his answer all polished up. Then he opened his mouth and what came out was not what I expected.

"No, Ron, we're not, and I do have some thoughts on your question, but I don't think you're ready for them, so hold the question and we'll get to it later in my story, OK?"

(Damn!) "OK."

"Anyhow, there I was, a one-man Syrian-American army marching through Texas and then through New Mexico. I had made a typical-for-me wandering route through Texas, sticking to country roads and going off-course a few times when my drivers were making turns that didn't feel like detours at the moment. I think that when I got near Corpus Christi and crossed into New Mexico I'd been on the road for more than six weeks, maybe two months. Fatigue had long since set in, but the idea that my journey was about three-quarters done was encouraging. I have to say that having never been out of the Northeast before, everything was still new to me. I was surprised that the road network of Texas was such a hodge-podge of country two-lanes going this way and that, which slowed my progress and gave me more frightening nights than I anticipated.

"I have to say I don't remember much about New Mexico. There were mountains, of course, where West Texas was only referred to as 'hill country,' but being blind I didn't get to enjoy the vistas. In fact I was pretty lucky because when we got into New Mexico near Las Cruces and went west toward the Black Range on a state road that runs as Interstate 10 through the state, I was lucky enough to get one ride almost all the way through the mountains. If I'd had to get out and walk through those peaks at night I might have become frozen food for some mountain cat. And of course now that I was in the southwest I was snake-scared way beyond copperheads. There were rattlers out here, and even those terrorized me less than coral snakes, which I had read back in fourth grade could kill me in about two minutes, and had no rattles to warn me they were angry.

"I was reminded several times to concentrate as hard as I could on my hearing and other senses, especially when I went off a road surface to find a place to relieve myself or go to sleep. In Texas, and also in New Mexico and Arizona there was far less forest, and it was much quieter. I also had to take extra precautions to avoid getting lost while finding a place to sleep or getting back to the road in the morning, because it would be a lot easier to get lost forever out there. There were several times I sensed I'd have to make really tiny steps, for fear that the next step might be a hundred feet down. I had to move really slowly and memorize my steps going off the road and coming back.

"Happily though, I did get a few rides, and a couple of them were longer, so much of New Mexico passed by in the comfort of a front seat in a heated car or pick-up truck."

"So all this fear of snakes and no snakes?" I asked.

"I'm coming to that. West of New Mexico is Arizona.

"Another week later I was seriously cutting down on my eating. I'd long since finished my stash of Hershey bars, my little memory of home, and I was down to about one sandwich a day to try to conserve my last few dollars. All through Texas, New Mexico and Arizona I also had to be careful to ration my water, as there just weren't a lot of places to stop and fill my jug, especially for free.

"In Arizona I was trying to make a more direct route through the southern part of the state, going as close to due-west as I could, maybe a hundred fifty miles south of Flagstaff, and again staying pretty clear of the cities – my experience getting lost in Hershey on the third day of my trip had really made me fearful of repeat experiences in other large towns or cities.

"On my third, or maybe fourth day in Arizona, I'd gotten picked up by an old fellow driving an even older big rig truck and we were heading west just south of the Painted Desert area. The day was almost warm, the sun was bright (I was told) and the road surface itself must have been nice and warm for winter. In that part of the country even when the days grew warm, the air cooled rapidly in the evenings and got pretty frigid at night.

"As we moved down the road, the driver slowed down suddenly, because we were going over some strange bumps, which seemed out of place. The driver let out a whole string of exclamations, and slowed down even further. After a few more bumps the engine started coughing and sputtering. I asked what the problem was, and the driver answered with two words that sent shivers up and down my spine.

"Damn snakes!" he said. "Can't you see 'em?"

"I couldn't help it. My greatest fear was immediately up in my throat and my heart was going faster than the truck's engine. After everything I'd already been through, snakes were the one thing I had avoided meeting, even though every night I had to sleep outside I shivered at the prospect of even one snake being nearby.

"Once again I had chosen not to reveal my blindness, but now had to admit to it, though I wouldn't be surprised if I stuttered and stumbled a bit getting the words out.

"Christ Almighty! I said. How many of them are there?"

"Must be at least thirty or forty just behind us now, and you can bet there'll be more up ahead."

It was my worst nightmare. It seems the snakes were happily soaking up the heat of the asphalt. Being cold-blooded, I could imagine it was welcome comfort to them, though more than dangerous for me at the same time. Some of them must have been long and fat, given the bumps the old truck was absorbing.

"What are we going to do?" I asked.

"Well, we sure as shit ain't going to turn tail and head back east!" he said. "I'll try to get around 'em rather than over top of 'em. I'm not sure how many bounces and bumps this old truck can handle."

"You can imagine how I felt when I heard him say that. In some ways if you had the same fear of snakes that I have, it might have been worse for you, because you could see them, but let me tell you, I was sweating bullets despite the chill that night."

I could relate. I've never seen thirty snakes at once except in that really creepy scene in one of the Indiana Jones flicks, but just the thought of seeing thirty at once on a nice warm strip of Arizona asphalt, soaking up the warmth of the asphalt while getting run over by old cars and trucks is vivid enough for me. Actually, I've never been to one of those churches where the preacher performs snake-handling for whatever message that's supposed to have for the faithful, but if I ever attend one of those services I can pretty well bet right now I'll be leader of the pack leaving the church in the middle of the sermon.

"OK," I said. "I get the picture – and it's not a pretty one for me either. So what did you do?"

"Well, remember Ron, I wasn't driving, and I certainly wasn't going to ask the old guy to stop so I could get out right then. He weaved us back and forth, trying to avoid as many as he could, but we still bumped over a few more and then there was a hill on our left which would have put us into a patch of shade in the daytime, and on which the road surface must have been much cooler, so that stretch was clear. It was when we got out onto a straight patch we found another batch of snakes, and these must have been clustered together, I guess, so they were unavoidable. That's when a bad dream turned into a nightmare."

"Uh-oh…" I said softly. "The old truck broke down."

"Precisely."

That was all he needed to say. I was in the nightmare with him.

"I give up. What did you do then?"

(I could imagine him trying to get out and tip-toe around among two or three dozen snakes on a cozy moonbath, which were not looking to be disturbed. I'd have peed my pants…and I can see! Joe wouldn't know how to tip-toe, or at least which way to tip and which way to toe. Two thousand four hundred and eleventy miles against all odds and then to be snakebit about twenty times in twenty seconds. What a concept!)

Joe smiled, but this memory was probably one of the most haunting in his entire brain.

"Well, you know I had worked in auto repair ever since high school, and I believed I knew as much as anyone about how car and truck engines work, even diesels, how they sound, how to get them back on the road, and so on. The old man just pounded his fists on the steering wheel and muttered curses. I screwed up all the courage I imagined I had and opened my door, stepped out on the running board, and slowly climbed out onto the truck's front fender. I was going to try to raise that side of the engine hood and see what I could see that might be causing the truck to stall out and not fire up again. You can bet my whole body was shaking, and not just little nervous twitches, either. I guess I was out there for about ten minutes when God arrived in the person of another semi driver. He stopped and laughed at us, which my driver thought was neither nice nor funny. But then he did offer us a ride to the nearest service station.

"At first, I was determined to refuse the ride. I just wanted to climb back into the truck, close the windows and wait there for a mechanic to get us restarted, but the other semi-driver had no idea how far it would be to the next service station, so I let my new/old friend assure me that he'd guide me over to the other semi, which was only a few steps, without stepping on any scaly thing with fangs. I can tell you I didn't take a single breath and my feet were on fire!

We got going in the cab of the second semi and I noticed more bumps as we crushed a few more snakes, and sure enough it was nearly twenty miles before we hit the next town and service station. The station's mechanic agreed to drive back to the truck that originally picked me up, shoot as many snakes as necessary, and see if he could get it going again. I decided to stay there at the station and eat a ketchup sandwich and wait for him to bring me back my suitcase. It was as close as I ever wanted to be to an extended family of those creatures."

I exhaled. A few times.

"You know, Joe, this whole story has been a really long trip through a house of horrors. In a way it seems like it must be total fiction, because here you are sitting across from me, calm as a jet pilot, telling me about it like it was a walk in the park. And how long have you been living on ketchup sandwiches by this point?"

Joe smiled. "About eleven weeks, I guess. When I got to Los Angeles, I weighed myself once after about a week of being there, and I weighed ninety four pounds. If someone called me 'wiry' it would have been a compliment."

"Damn! That means you'd have already lost more than twenty-five pounds, maybe thirty-five! So much for bread being the 'staff of life,' don't you think?

"I won't deny it, Ron. The journey was no picnic. If I'd known what I know now about the trip, I doubt I'd have attempted it, even though I can remember as clear as glass that there was no other way for me, nothing else I would do. I just had to go, period."

I drove home that afternoon thinking about his last statement. Brains? Not exactly. Research? None. Reasonable planning and thought? Huh-uh. Preparation? Budgeting? Practice? Are you kidding?

Yet he did it, and he's been sitting in his semi-palatial living room telling me all about it for days now. What he had was determination – in massive amounts, and I'm sure he had doubts, and even some clear-headed fears of dying along the way across the country, but what determination!

I didn't know what to do with any of it. In fact I couldn't find any way to connect with Joe's experience and use what I'd learned to kick my own life into gear. Still, it occurred to me that it was time for me to do something. Anything. And right now, without any more moping around or searching for some brilliant flash of inspiration.

What actually happened was that God whacked me upside the head. How do I know it was God? I'll explain and you tell me if you have any other explanation. I was driving down Route 250 in Staunton and stopped at a stoplight. My car's radio was on, an AM station playing country songs. They'd just finished five songs and launched into a three-minute commercial break. The first ad was for Martin's Supermarket, which had a job opening for a food preparation person, part-time leading to full-time with "great salary, full Martins' benefits including tuition assistance, and a career's worth of opportunity!!!"

So how was this a whack from God? Three facts: (1) I'd just made up my mind to do something; (2) I'd just tuned in to hear this help wanted ad; and (3) the stoplight was right in front of Staunton's Martin's store. You tell me.

Miracle or not, I pulled into the Martin's lot and went in. I asked about the job, filled out their three-page application form, presented it to the Store Manager, talked with him for about ten minutes, and shook hands, smiling. He would be checking my references (two) and my police record (none), but I was to report for work the following Monday.

When I got back in the car and turned the key I almost threw up. My brain was exploding with the sonic boom of what I had just done. Suddenly there were thirty-seven questions, a hundred and ten doubts, and one big sense that I had just done a very stupid thing. Hence the hurl.

What the hell do I know about cooking food? What do I know about customer service? What possible connection does any job in a Martin's Supermarket have to do with a career, and making a fortune, and driving a Porsche and having three or four kids and being respected?

So I opened my car door and made a small mess on the pavement, grabbed three McDonald's napkins from the passenger seat, wiped my face and pulled out. I was actually sweating, and feeling ocean waves of embarrassment and wondering how I could explain my failure to show up on Monday morning for my first day of training.

When I got home the waves were still washing over my head like a hot tsunami, and I avoided my Mom entirely, hit the bathroom and locked the door. It took me a small eternity to calm down and convince myself that I could find a way out of my miracle before Monday, so for tonight mum was the word. I would talk with Joe tomorrow morning. Mrs. Joe had promised Syrian treats for lunch.

Chapter Thirteen
A Turning Point

"Welcome back, Ron! Ready for the last leg of my journey?"

Joe seemed in good spirits when I arrived, though I wasn't sure I could say the same thing about myself. I had decided not to bring up my "God Moment" yesterday until he was finished today. It was a good decision.

"Yesterday we were in Arizona and I had my visit with my personal devils."

"I remember," I said. "Only too clearly!"

He laughed. "Well, after that little adventure, things began to change. I had some more walking to do and some more wandering off my route. Weather was no longer as much of a problem, but my budget was nearly exhausted, and I wasn't eating every day. I had grown accustomed to a habit of hunger, but it was getting worse.

"Anyway, I did get picked up once by a truck driver who was friendlier than usual. While he was heading in my general direction, he had several deliveries to make, and I agreed to help him with them. That took me on a bit of wandering, so I didn't make as much progress toward Los Angeles as I might have hoped.

"Los Angeles?" I asked. "So you finally decided on a destination? Why LA? Did you suddenly develop a Hollywood dream?"

Joe laughed again. The man either has a great sense of humor or he's just really kind, laughing at my attempts at humor even if they're not always respectful.

"Actually I had two reasons for focusing on Los Angeles. The first came to me when I had to turn south in Indianapolis to get out of the snow and closed roads. It actually hadn't occurred to me until that night that if I'd stayed on that due-west route I'd have had to cross the Rocky Mountains in the middle of winter, on foot and with no money for shelter. That wasn't very bright of me, was it?"

"And the second?"

"My second reason was I had relatives in Los Angeles – well one relative, a cousin. In our family, that meant I could hope for at least a meal or two and perhaps more help in getting myself going with some kind of job and place to live. I missed my family in Pennsylvania, and even just the chance to get on a phone and call them seemed like quite a gift – a gift that my $28 budget hadn't permitted so far."

"OK, back to your Arizona travels."

"Right. I had one experience, and only one, with a person you might call a lowlife, or even a criminal. One driver in Arizona picked me up and then picked up another hitchhiker shortly after me. We drove for more than an hour when the driver pulled into a service station for gas and went inside to pay. I'd been carrying on a conversation with him and the other hitchhiker, and I remember getting a little edgy about the hitchhiker, who never even gave his name or shook hands. I had no idea what he looked like, of course, but he was no conversationalist, and what little he said sounded less than sociable.

"While the driver was inside paying for his gas, the other hitchhiker suggested we ask him to stop outside of town somewhere and when he did, we would beat him up and take the car. He obviously didn't know about my blindness, but that was pretty frightening. I told him that I wanted no part of his idea, and developed a sudden need to use the service station bathroom. When I got into the station I found the driver and told him about the other guy's intention. When he came out, he ordered the fellow out of his car and the two of us left. For a moment I thought the other guy was going to attack him right there in the station, but he just cursed the driver and me and got out.

"So let me see if I understand. You've been on the road now for more than two months. You've lost a major bunch of weight due to ketchup and white bread not being the 'staff of life.' You've been bitten by a poisonous spider, caught a hell of a cold or pneumonia, gotten lost about a hundred times, frozen yourself to near death in both snow and rain, found yourself in an entire world of poisonous snakes, and you're still walking in a pair of loafers that must have needed new soles by now…oh, and you're still not in California, although your $28 has long since burned a hole in your wallet. Do I have it right?"

Joe actually closed his eyes and dropped his head for a moment. When he spoke, his voice was softer than usual.

"You do, and my feelings about the whole of my journey are complicated. By the time I got to the Arizona border and entered California, on the one hand I was excited, almost happy, and I began thinking about a strategy for starting my life as a blind man. At the same time I was really hungry and way too used to being hungry, and exhausted too, not just by the lack of sleep, but by the constant need to concentrate so hard every minute of every day to keep myself alive. There were maybe a hundred times when I was walking along a road and a vehicle came up behind me and passed me too closely. I could have been hit quite easily on virtually any day of the journey, so I was way beyond mentally exhausted."

He stopped there, and neither of us said anything for a several minutes, both of us lost in a kind of meditation on the whole of his journey experience. The every-minute challenge of his blindness, so much physical suffering, so much fear and danger and yet so much determination and will. I was in awe of it, and of him.

I opened my mouth first.

"Joe, I know you're nearing the end of your journey, and I know you made it. I want to hear much more about the journey you started once you got to Los Angeles, but I need to interrupt the story for a bit…to ask for your help…for me.

"Sure, Ron. What do you need?"

It was suddenly terribly hard even to start. It was as if I had to speak in Syrian, or whatever Syrians speak.

"I did something on my way home yesterday, and I – I'm kind of – shaken up by it."

He sat very still and by that stillness I could sense that he was listening with that incredible concentration that had helped him survive for three months on the road.

"I applied for a job…

…and I got it."

Joe nearly exploded. His smile was the widest I'd seen on his face in all our conversations, and he reached for me to congratulate me.

"That's wonderful, Ron! Wonderful! Tell me!"

"Not so fast, Joe. I don't know if it's wonderful at all, and part of me thinks it's stupid and dumb and I'm not even sure I want to report for work next Monday."

He sat back slowly, his smile fading, but the look on his face was a strange mix of things, among which, I hoped, was understanding.

"My job is preparing cooked food in Martin's Supermarket. You know, like rotisserie chickens and pizzas and salads and stuff. I'm kind of short-order cook for long orders. It's a job, but the radio commercial I heard in my car said it was a 'career opportunity' and I kind of feel that's laughable. I'm embarrassed and even the fact that I got the job so easily seems like proof of my stupidity...I mean --"

"Stop!"

That was all he said, but he practically shouted it, and I was stunned. I'd never seen him angry in the least bit, but the look on his face was a sudden thunderstorm. His one word command reverberated through the room in a long moment of silence.

"So," he said, much more softly. "—what did you want from me about this?"

It was a simple question, but one that was suddenly very had to answer.

"Your opinion…your thoughts, I guess."

He lowered his head again, a sign that he was thinking before speaking. It was a sign that made me listen extra carefully to what came next.

"Alright. I will give you my thoughts, but when I have done that, I don't want you to respond, or ask any more questions today. Just listen to what I say to you and go home and think about it. Will you do that?"

"OK." I felt like I was twenty-two going on twelve. This is what he said.

"I have two things to say to you. The first is about yourself. The second is about the job you were given, and the work you will do in it if you decide to go ahead with it.

"First, I have learned a bit about you. At this point in your life you are perhaps more uncertain about yourself and how you are to live your life than you have ever been or will ever be again. Somehow you have learned to doubt yourself pretty profoundly, and the doubt is paralyzing. There is no great cosmic truth in the doubt. You are a full-fledged human being, with a unique basket of skills, intelligence, gifts, talents, and imperfections that make you Ron Brantley. Nothing more, nothing less. You are not Mike Trout, MVP of the Angels and you are not a drug dealer and murderer. You are just a man – as I am just a man. A child of God just as I am. There are plenty of reasons for you to believe in yourself as a child of God, a child with all the potential to be successful in life that anyone else has -- and there are plenty of reasons for you to be decently humble about yourself at the same time.

"Second, about the job. It is work. The job you applied for exists because people want and need the product you will produce and the service you will provide -- and are willing to pay for it. All work...I mean a-l-l work...is worthy of respect. The value of any work lies less in the work itself than in what you bring to the work. If you concern yourself only with what the work will offer you, you may find little reason to be excited by it, even if it is starring in a movie or playing baseball. But consider what will happen from the things you bring to the work. Bring it your attention, your energy, your concentration, your ability to learn, and even your love, and watch how you transform the work.

"I started in Los Angeles by stacking boards at a lumber mill, then filling gas tanks and washing windshields at a service station. Most people would call those low-level, nothing jobs if ever there was one, and unworthy of anything more than a minimum wage insufficient to support even one man, much less a family. I brought more of myself to that job than simply my ability to sweep a squeegee across a plate of glass. I was willing to learn, to become an expert, to add value to my employer's business, and finally to start my own business. Today here we sit. Am I smarter than you? More talented? More creative? None of these. I am simply another child of our loving God who is generous with his gifts and his forgiveness when we squander those gifts for a time.

"Stop beating yourself up. Give yourself a chance. But stop waiting for the world to give you things and focus instead on what you can give to the world through your own gifts. On Monday the gift you bring to Martin's may be only the ability to learn to tie a chicken before putting it on a rotisserie. On Tuesday it will be something else. On

Wednesday you may learn to stir mayonnaise into tuna salad with a smile on your face, and discover that customers smile back at you. A month later you may discover that you actually have an interest in food preparation, and even the creativity to become a cook, and then a chef or even a restaurateur. Throughout the process you will find yourself learning new things, building new skills, becoming more and more valuable to the work you do and to your employer…until one day you are the employer, and teaching others the lessons you have learned.

"Go home now and think about what I've said. If you come back tomorrow I will tell you about my arrival in Los Angeles and the beginnings of my career. It's a good bit different from my travel experiences."

Chapter Fourteen

City of Angels

So…how did I feel on my way home, you ask?

It's not easy to describe. I heard Joe's last statements echoing in my brain, and even laughed once when his phrase "echo-location" popped into my mind. I had to admit to myself that what he said was probably more true than false, more right than wrong (OK, damn it, he was right!) and my own thoughts and feelings were pretty much horse-hockey. I had spent the last few years of my life looking through the prism of Ron Brantley, as if the only things that mattered were what I thought, how I felt, what the world was giving me or withholding, etc. Yes, Virginia, I have an ego in the very center of my brain and it can make for a really cloudy windshield.

So OK, I'm going to work on Monday. And yes, I'm going to stop worrying that my brain isn't adequate to the job of life and just learn how to do my job well enough to earn a few smiles and a few bucks.

But I also felt kind of beaten up. Kind of small and stupid. It wasn't a good feeling, and it hurt in several places in my head and other parts. I guess that is guilt and embarrassment for all the time I've been wallowing in my own fear that I'm not enough.

The more I thought about that, the more I realized that those fears were making me their prisoner. Joe Cory said he believes I'm as capable as anyone, or at least that I need to throw off the handcuffs of my fears of inadequacy and start learning what it takes to succeed.

No, I'm not going to become Mike Trout of the Angels or Muhammad Ali. But chances are I can be Ron Brantley, functional human being.

When I arrived at Joe's house the next morning, he met me at his front door and just stood still for a moment, his eyes staring into mine. He wasn't seeing anything with those eyes, but I swear he was "seeing" a great deal, somehow, in my face, or the way I was standing there, or maybe he was using 'echo-location' up close and personal, because he smiled with what looked like a kind of recognition, that maybe I'd broken through the wall of my own little prison, or something like that. (My I'm getting romantic here, aren't I?)

He held out his hand and I gave him mine. Maybe it was his sense of touch, or maybe he heard the vibrations of that moment, but he smiled a great smile and suddenly the clouds parted and a cascade of sunlight came down and a choir of angels broke out and…oh well, shit, you get the picture.

"Come in, come in. My journey is just about over and my next journey is about to begin."

When we had settled downstairs in his living room I waited for him to begin. He was silent for a few seconds, so I prodded him.

"So, Joe, you landed in LA and on your first morning the beach was hit by a tsunami and it washed you back to Indianapolis…"

112

He laughed out loud, and so did I. When I exhaled, it felt like the first time in months.

"OK, Ron! No, there was no tsunami. The closer I got to town, the better I was feeling, even though I had to pay even greater attention to my surroundings, to traffic sounds, road and shoulder surfaces, and things like that as traffic suddenly started growing around me.

"I got one of my last rides from a man who lived in the LA suburbs. I told him I'd be looking for work, and again I didn't tell him I was blind, but –"

"—Excuse me, Joe, but there that is again. Why the efforts to hide your blindness? I don't understand that!"

He stopped for a minute, gathering his thoughts. "I realize that on some levels that doesn't seem to make sense, but to me it did, for a number of reasons. First of all, I had been dealing with my blindness for almost three and a half months now, and with all I'd been through, I was pretty confident that I was surviving…more than surviving really. I'd driven a car almost a hundred miles, I'd avoided wild animals and survived awful weather, slept outside on many nights, made nearly three thousand miles on twenty-eight bucks, and so on. Second, I'd learned a hard lesson the few times I did let it slip that I was blind. People didn't respond very positively to that at all. In fact, a couple of times I'm pretty sure it made a driver ask me to get out earlier than I'd hoped. You can understand, I'm sure, that nobody feels as comfortable even just talking with a handicapped person as they do with others. I'm convinced that a number of men who picked me up were instantly hesitant, and even careful in their conversation with me. Phrases like 'look at that' and 'did you see that truck?' were suddenly off-limits, even embarrassing to them. Then there was often the impulse to feel sympathy for me – as someone less fortunate than themselves, but even that made them uncomfortable. I don't think I benefitted from revealing my blindness even once. On the other hand, I'm sure I'd been able to strike up a good conversation and even start up a few dozen momentary friendships with men who'd let me join them.

"Anyway, this one fellow who gave me a ride through Palm Springs and into the LA suburbs dropped me off pretty close to downtown. I had nothing but my suitcase, and even pictures of food made my stomach growl. I didn't have to search for billboard runners to sleep on, figuring rats and stray dogs were probably the worst things I needed to worry about, but when I was dropped off on the edge of a big city park my blindness kind of reared up and gave me the seriously lost feeling that I'd already suffered several times on my way across the country. I slept on park benches at first, because aside from hunger, exhaustion was my number two affliction. I did my best to stay reasonably presentable, but with no money for a hotel room, that was difficult. After about three days I asked passersby for directions to the State Department of Employment. I had to have help filling out my application, and had to stand in a long line, but when I reached the staff member's desk, she referred me to a lumber yard not too far away. I walked most of the way, getting help from other people at street corners, and when I reached the yard you can bet my concentration on my other senses was at an all-time high!

"I had to ratchet it up still higher, but was able to walk in, find a manager and ask for a job without any trouble. The interview lasted about thirty seconds, and I was able to stow my suitcase and start stacking boards, sorting them by length. I couldn't do it by sight, like the other men, but I could walk the board, count the paces, then match others and stack them accordingly. I must have done alright, because the work lasted three days before the boss began to suspect that I had eye problems. A couple of times I came close to getting run over by the yard's motorized forklifts, and although I'd done well enough stacking boards, I wasn't as quick as some of the other guys, so the manager told me he'd have to let me go. But he paid me $23 for three days work, and you can imagine how welcome that was, nestled in my pocket!

"So you finally came to the end of ketchup sandwiches?"

"By then I'd have been grateful even for a ketchup sandwich, but I did!" he said with a smile. "I'm not sure I've eaten one since! Still, I didn't want to spend all my new money right away. I needed a place to live and a steady job, and at that moment everything was new and the ability to concentrate my senses (other than sight) were even more crucial in the city. I made my way into Hollywood, I got directions to the cheapest motel, and rented a room for two nights. You can't imagine how great it was to get a shower and clean my clothes in a laundromat!

"So things were looking up?" I asked.

"They were. I've thought many times since '55 that it was actually lucky I made that left turn at Indianapolis a couple of months earlier."

"Why is that?"

"If I'd landed in San Francisco or Sacramento, there was no one there I could call on for help. But in LA I had a cousin, Jeannie, living in Canoga Park, about thirty-five miles

115

outside of downtown. I hitch hiked to her area and it took a while, but I found her house and knocked on her door.

"She must have been surprised!" I could just picture young Joe standing there, and her having no idea he was blind, or that he'd even left Allentown.

"She was, but she gave me a big hug and invited me in. When her husband Jim came home from work, he was a little less overwhelmed with joy, but he was friendly as well."

"Did you ask them for help?"

"As a matter of fact, I did. I told them I needed a place to stay, and after a short discussion they said they had a bedroom I could stay in. Her husband agreed I could stay, but he wasn't going to simply give the room away. He asked for rent for the room, seven dollars a week if I remember, which I agreed to. When I said I'd been working as an auto and truck mechanic back in Pennsylvania, he brightened up and asked if I could do some work on his Studebaker, which was running very badly. Neither of them knew I was blind, at least at first, and when I revealed it, both were more than a little surprised.

"The Studebaker work turned out to be a…I was going to say 'coincidence,' but I should have said a kind of God-send. The next day Jim took me downtown in the car, and it really was barely running. He pulled into a service station owned by a man he knew pretty well, and the owner agreed to let me work on the car in one of his bays when I had time. A couple of days later, as he watched me breaking down the car's engine, I told him I was looking for work, and he also gave me a tip on a job down the street, doing welding.

"Welding? A blind man welding? Next you're going to tell me you were hired to call balls and strikes for the Dodgers!"

Joe smiled. "That would be impossible, Ron. They were still playing in Ebbetts Field – in Brooklyn. But given the chance, I probably could have worked on learning to use 'echo-location' to 'hear' the pitches coming in and get most of the calls right! (I chuckled, and so did he....)

"Anyway, I got started welding, and was able to earn more money from those two jobs. That first work and the paychecks that came with it really picked up my spirits. The welding work only lasted two weeks though, because putting the welding torch up against my face to "see" a tiny part of the torch's flame, I burned off my eyebrows and much of the skin on my face was getting burned as well.

"In fact, it might have been the damage that welding torch did to my face that resulted in my eyes getting glued shut. That was pretty alarming, and I tried to see a doctor, but I still didn't have enough money to pay for his services. I did get to see one doctor, who was able to open my eyes again, but rather than treat me any further himself, he suggested pretty strongly that I get myself to the UCLA Hospital. I tried, but the people at the hospital refused to see me because I had no money."

"What happened then?" I asked.

"Well, the doctor who referred me made a call for me and reminded the hospital people about the recent piece of really bad publicity another hospital had earned by refusing to see another patient in its emergency room until his wife drove home and returned with cash. The man died sitting on a bench waiting for her return, and it hit all the papers.

117

"Wow!" I said. It had become one of my patented responses.

"So the hospital did admit me, and the doctors and examined my eyes. They decided to try an experimental treatment, injecting me with typhoid fever…"

"What?!" I asked. "Why in the world would they do that?"

"They thought that typhoid might actually increase the blood flow to my eyes, especially my retinas and optic nerve. It didn't restore my sight, which would have been a major miracle, but after a week in the hospital I found that I could, now and then, see a pinpoint of white light that was shined right into my eye, for perhaps a second at a time. After seeing nothing for several months, even that was exciting to me, and I worked on that tiny 'sight' for years to expand it into seeing part of one letter of a single word, then another part. Even with that progress, which I thought was a near-miracle, it would have taken me thirty minutes or more to 'read' a single paragraph, so by all measures I have remained blind ever since."

"You realize, Joe, I'm beginning to get the impression you'd do anything for money, blind or not!"

"Well, it may seem like that was my motivation, but I still didn't have the means to begin leading my own life, so making money was important, but I also had a belief that I could do almost anything in the world of work, blind or not, and so far that belief had sustained me.

"A few days after I'd taken residence in my cousin's home in Canoga Park, my sister back in Pennsylvania sent me a check for a hundred dollars that I'd been owed by the man who bought my service station in Allentown. That was another piece of good fortune, and it didn't take me long to figure out what to do with it. With that check, plus my earnings from welding, I had Jim take me down to a used car lot where I bought myself a wounded 1940 Ford for about $75, so I could start getting around on my own."

"You've got to be kidding! Blind Joe – driving again?!"

I must have conveyed a bit more than mere surprise. In fact I really thought he was nuts to drive that car 100 miles on his way across the country, and now he's in downtown Los Angeles and its suburbs –with his own car! I tried to imagine attempting to drive myself with Joe's sleep mask on, and I remembered the fumbles and bumped knees I'd incurred just trying to walk to his bathroom ten feet away. Anyhow, my exclamation must have registered in Joe's brain as disapproval, and he was quiet for a couple of minutes.

"I hope you will believe me when I say I wasn't playing around, and I certainly wasn't carelessly threatening harm to anyone else. I truly believed I could drive safely as long as I took extraordinary care every minute behind the wheel.

"I hadn't had an accident of any kind, Ron, either when crossing the country, in California, or back east when I came home. I'll admit any driving I might have tried to do at all required that I take several steps before I could do it successfully. For example, in California I would get a little help from Jim in memorizing my routes, including all stop signs and turns, stoplights, and crosswalks. I would walk through the neighborhood, concentrating extra hard on the sounds of traffic, and even people walking by. I knew I'd have to drive my old Ford with the windows wide open so I could hear virtually all the details of traffic movement around me, and I've already explained how hard I had worked to remain totally focused, concentrating on even the

119

smallest shred of information that might come to me through my other senses. I was no NASCAR racer or anything, but I could get to the station where I was working and back home with little trouble. My Pennsylvania driver's license was still good, and if I'd ever been stopped by a traffic cop, I would have been frightened, but I believed I could pretty much handle the stop without being found out. It sounds contradictory, I know, but understand that I was taking extraordinary care every minute I was behind the wheel, paying far more attention to my surroundings and other traffic than the average driver."

"Yeah-h-h, maybe, but I don't know, Joe. When I put on Mrs. Cory's sleep mask, and try to imagine driving anywhere, especially in a city, well…I can't even imagine it. And you did this for how long?"

"Most of four years, Ron."

"Damn!"

It was beyond my imagination.

"I mean that's a huge achievement, and I can understand how listening as hard as you had learned to do can make up for at least some of what you weren't seeing, but…but it still seems a bit…you know, a bit crazy!"

There was silence, and it seemed to last forever. I could sense that for the first time there was a distance between Joe and me, and I could feel that distance without seeing a thing.

Finally, he started again, working to convince me that what he'd been doing was both possible, and even reasonable.

"-- Let me give you a couple of examples. First of all, I would memorize neighborhoods I was driving in, and develop a good sense of how long blocks were and where intersections and traffic lights were. I would follow a vehicle in front of me at a distance close enough to hear it slow down, stop or speed up. Second, I drove mostly between my apartment and the station where I worked. If I was approaching a stoplight, and the vehicle in front of me suddenly accelerated, I'd know he was trying to get through the intersection before the light turned red. In short order I slowed down, pulled over to the curb and stopped, and then waited for an opportunity to join the flow again when traffic behind me had gaps and the vehicles going by me were traveling at a steady speed – which meant green light. I'm sure I paid more attention to my surroundings and other traffic than any sighted driver on the road.

"Only once in all my time in California did a motorcycle cop pull abreast of me in the left lane and stayed alongside of me for a couple of blocks. You can bet I was hyper-alert for the first opportunity to make a right turn while he went straight ahead through the intersection. At no time would I describe myself as any kind of 'comfortable' or 'casual' about my responsibility behind the wheel, and at no time did I have the least accident of any kind."

By Joe's tone, I knew he was serious and wasn't about to hear my objections. I had some, but thought better of offering them. The issue was, as they say, "in the rearview mirror" anyway.

"OK, Joe, let's get back to your life in LA -- when you weren't behind the wheel."

"Sure. As I told you, three things happened in pretty rapid succession. My few days of stacking lumber ended before I was ready, but I was paid enough to get myself out to

Hollywood, rent a motel room for two nights, clean myself and my clothes, and then hitchhike out to Canoga Park where I called on my cousin, Jeannie. She was really surprised to see me on her doorstep with no advance notice, but when her husband Jim got home from work and we were eating dinner, I asked if I could stay with them for a few weeks until I could find work and get a place of my own. They agreed to let me have one of their bedrooms for $7 a week rent, which also covered whatever meals I was present for. I still had about $13 so I could pay for my first week, and that evening's spaghetti dinner my first in months. I must have eaten at least three helpings. While we were eating, I told Jim that I'd been an auto mechanic back in Pennsylvania where I owned my own station. He was happy to learn that, and quickly had me working on his broken down Studebaker. I was happy to say 'yes!' and the next day he drove me to his friend's service station downtown and arranged for me to do a complete overhaul on the car's engine in one of the station's service bays. He paid me for the work, which took me a week, so I soon had a few more dollars, and ketchup sandwiches were becoming a mere memory."

"So things were looking up…finally!"

"They were, and my good fortune didn't stop there! After working on the welding job for about two and a half weeks I had even more money. When I had to quit welding, and after my hospital stay, the service station owner kind of took pity on me and offered me work at his station. He wanted me to serve his customers at the gas pumps, filling tanks, checking oil and squee-geeing windshields. Even though he'd seen me work on Jim's car, he didn't believe yet that I could do the work of his mechanics, but at least I could free them up to work inside while I took care of customers outside. He said he couldn't pay me, but he'd give me a room behind the station and a cheeseburger for lunch each day."

"Wowee-Zowee!" I said, (dripping with cynicism.) "What an offer! Eight hours work for a cheeseburger! Did you tell him where he could stick it?"

"No, I didn't. I didn't want to stay out in the suburbs for long, and I knew I was a burden to my cousin. The offer gave me a place to stay, my own bed and bathroom, and a decent lunch. The work wasn't challenging, and I could do it easily. Despite that, it didn't work out so well, because several customers got unhappy with the idea of a blind man checking their crankcase, and wanted one of the owner's mechanics to do it."

"I'd hate to say this, but I might have agreed with them, especially without knowing you and all you'd been through," I said.

Joe chuckled. "Well anyway, consider, Ron. I now had a room with a bed for no rent, a decent lunch (there were French fries and a coke with the burger) and work that didn't involve acetylene torches. Plus I still had maybe $40 or so from the welding job and the Studebaker repair, so I wasn't trying to live on juts the cheeseburger. I hadn't wanted to be a burden to my cousin, who actually moved one of her two sons into his brother's room in order to let me use his room. Furthermore, I really wanted to be closer to downtown and Hollywood, rather than out in Canoga Park, which was a good thirty-five miles outside of town, so the station owner's offer looked pretty good. Besides, I had watched the two mechanics who worked for him, and I was pretty sure I could do their work as well or better than they were doing it. So in between filling tanks for gas customers, I had plenty of chances to chat with them in the bays and offer suggestions to help them make more successful repairs. It didn't take long for the owner to notice all that, and in about two more weeks, he offered me a full-time job as a mechanic, with pretty decent pay."

I had to admit, at least to myself, that Joe was doing pretty well for himself, but there was more, and because he'd mentioned Hollywood two or three times, I was interested in that for other reasons.

Jackie interrupted to offer refreshments and join the conversation for a few minutes, and once again I was impressed by a fact that was right in front of my eyes, but somehow remained more than a little mysterious to me.

How can a seriously intelligent, wholly attractive woman of independent means and a good paying career fall for a blind man? And I don't just mean "fall for him" because I know Joe was a good looking, studly dude when he was younger, but Joe has to be eighty-two now and the evidence is right before my eyes: she's still falling for him forty-nine years later!

I have nothing against Joe, and in fact I find him to be a gentleman in every respect, and the fact that the two of them are still together after 49 years of marriage is crystal clear. Still, I wonder how it can happen, given the inevitable burden she bears of caring for a blind person day and night for all that time. Doesn't it get old? Doesn't she get tired of the thousand little interventions and "assistances" that Joe needs each day? I can't figure it out, and maybe it's my limited experience, but I just wonder how it works for them.

I sensed I'd have to ask him about that, but now wasn't the time.

Having postponed that question, I should admit without hesitation that there is one explanation that is definitely beyond my experience. Maybe the two of them are just stone in love. I have to admit that simply isn't part of my life experience, and while I have dreamed about it many times, my imagination is a poor substitute for life experience. I should also admit that Joe has taken quite good care of Jackie for those forty-nine years, and not just by providing for her. He shows his affection, his respect, and his care for her in a hundred little ways each time I'm with them, but still, the thousand little "services" she performs each day to ease his life are beyond my imagination. I don't know the answer to this puzzle, but I can certainly hope what they found together happens to me, and please God, without me going blind.

We made a date for our next get-together and I headed home.

Chapter Fifteen
Not by Bread Alone…

The next time I sat with Joe, he told me about a series of events in Los Angeles that took him on a whole new ride up the ladder of his life. If I were a religious person, I'd have believed that God had decided to stop flogging him with the miseries, fears, and trials of a blind hitch-hiker, and began rewarding him for his determination, courage, and yes, even his faith.

I should stop here for a bit to report on what was going on in my own head. In hindsight, I remember noticing that the time I'd been spending with Joe had kind of worked its way into me pretty deeply, because I began to feel new thoughts breaking loose from the moss that had clogged my brain for several years.

I'd been working at Martin's for three and a half weeks, and it was no longer a shock to my system to get up in the morning and get to work – on-time even! I was already getting pretty familiar with most of my job tasks, so I no longer needed to start every sentence to my boss with "How do I…?" As a matter of fact, I'd already earned three or four compliments for my work, and while none of them came with a pay raise, they sure as hell bounced off the walls of my noggin like cannon-shot echoes in a canyon.

I'd never describe myself as over-confident, or even just medium-confident. For whatever reasons, I've grown up more or less certain that success in whatever contests I decide to enter is something I can dream about, but never actually experience. I can't begin to explain that. My parents were never down on me to any serious degree, and in fact gave me decent measures of praise as well as criticism, but in the daily contests of growing-up-life that I'd endured, I don't remember ever achieving anything beyond "honorable mention," if that. Never once did I get the gold, silver, or bronze. As you can probably understand, that experience in the day-to-day contests of life left me believing that "success" was something I'd only see through a glass, darkly.

Yet here I was these past several weeks, sitting with Joe Cory, listening to his life experiences, and getting really wrapped up in the contests of *his* life. Not only did he have to cope with personal challenges and impediments that I've never known. Not only did he decide to challenge himself with a journey that I wouldn't have attempted in a million of my own years. Joe attempted something that was beyond my imagination, faced a hundred challenges that would have had me hiding under my bed, and succeeded despite impediments I've never suffered.

I have to say that listening to him tell his story, actually experiencing it with him as he told it, has meant something to me way beyond entertainment. I've spent hours lying on my bed after my sessions with Joe, thinking about facing the very real fears he felt, and about the courage and determination that drove him westward for a hundred days and nearly three thousand miles…in the frigging winter of 1954/55, no less. What began to occur to me, slowly at first, was not so much that Joe is some kind of Ironman or Batman or Superman, as much as that he was a regular guy who just made a really hard decision and then reached inside and found the strength to turn that decision into a reality for himself.

It's funny, actually. I found myself building two impressions of him at once. First, of course, he grew to be a serious, world-class hero to me. But at the same time, I'm seeing him as just a guy Sid (well, OK, a guy Joe.) Like me. He's capable of making mistakes, suffering fears and setbacks and all the other confirmations that he's just a guy. Like me. When I'm through visiting with Joe and learning his story and becoming, hopefully, a friend for life, I'll take that with me.

But I'm getting ahead of myself.

I was anxious for this next session with Joe, and not because I was dying to hear any more about freezing and getting lost and snakes on the tarmac. I really wanted to hear about Joe Cory in Hollywood. He had taken time in a couple of earlier sessions to show me a few pictures of himself in his youth and despite blindness, Joe was a seriously good-looking male, at least when he'd had a couple of spaghetti dinners and double cheeseburgers nestled among his bones. I was curious to learn about his experiences in tinsel-town with all the females who had made their own journeys across the country to become starlets and stars and marry James Dean or Clark Gable.

"So…" he said when we were seated on his patio the next day. "…where were we?"

"In Hollywood!" I said quickly. "Running with stars and starlets, no doubt!"

He laughed, but not for long.

"Well, I'll get to that a bit later, but as I recall, I had a ways to go in getting myself set up out there to just survive in some kind of regular existence. If you remember, I'd spent a few nights sleeping on park benches in downtown Los Angeles, then three weeks renting a room in my cousin's house in Canoga Park, and finally finding work – and a place to sleep -- in the service station in Hollywood. I still didn't have a place of my own to live in, and even after I was starting to get paid as a welder and then a mechanic, I spent a couple of weeks sleeping behind the station or even in the back of my old Ford.

"Finally, I'd saved enough money to think about finding an apartment. By that time I'd met a girl who had taken an interest in me, and she offered to help me find a place to rent. She took me to a couple of places, and I decided pretty quickly on a second-floor efficiency in one of those Los Angeles places that looks a lot like a motel; one room which was actually pretty nice, with a tiny kitchen tucked into one corner, a little bathroom in another corner, and a long wall of shuttered doors. When I opened them, I found it was a closet, but it was full of women's clothing! -- which I wondered about, at least for a minute. As I was looking -- well, I mean feeling -- through the clothes, I heard a noise and the back wall of the closet opened up into a girl's apartment next door to mine!

"I was more than a little surprised, but I liked the place well enough, especially with two starlet wannabes as neighbors, and the rent was cheap enough for my budget at the time, so I took it."

"So Joe…" I asked. "Tell me about the girls – for example, the one that took an interest in you. Was she your girlfriend? I mean, did you two…uhh…?"

He smiled, but shook his head. "I really don't want to be Mister Kiss-and-Tell, even after 65 years, Ron, so let me put it this way. There were lots of girls in Hollywood, and yes I met several. As time went on and I began making more money, I began to have enough for a modest social life. I enjoyed myself, and yes, there were opportunities for romance and dating and relationships and fun. The weather was warm, the night life was what you might expect Hollywood to offer, and I was almost completely successful in hiding the fact that I was blind. So you could say I enjoyed myself. That's about as far as I want to go into that, OK?"

(Groan…)

"Meanwhile, back at the service station, my boss had noticed that I knew a good bit about working on cars after he'd watched me work on Jim's Studebaker. Even though I was blind, I could do valve grinding, honing cylinders, and basically rebuilding Jim's Studebaker engine in about a week, and I did it by sound and by touch. So after a couple of weeks working out front filling gas tanks and checking customers' oil, he let me start doing a little work in the bays, first on the lube rack, then tune-ups, brake repairs, and finally the bulk of mechanical work. He'd purchased a Sun Engine Diagnostic Machine, and I was able to help the other mechanics learn to use it in doing tune-ups and bigger repairs.

"When I was doing all of that, he began paying me $80 a week, which was pretty good, because my little apartment

130

was only $12 a week, so I was finally eating three meals a day in real restaurants and in my own little kitchen, and even having a girlfriend cook dinner for me now and then.

"Starting out with nothing more than a few coins in my pocket, it had taken me awhile to start earning anything like a living wage, but I did get there, and after working at that fellow's station for about six months, I had enough money to enroll in the General Motors Training Center in Reseda out in the Valley, in night classes where I learned a great deal about transmission repairs. I started by buying transmissions at junkyards so I could work on them in the station. I think it was my ability to really concentrate and focus my mind, which I'd learned on my trip across the country that accelerated my learning about transmissions. The work at the Training Center also gave me a good understanding of the *theory* of transmissions, how they were designed and how they worked.

"So, armed with that learning, I started doing transmission repair, which brought new business into the station. That gave me better pay, especially as I learned to fix virtually all the automatic transmissions on the road in those days. I was pretty proud of that. I could fix Hydramatic transmissions in Oldsmobiles and Cadillacs, Dynaflow transmissions in Buicks, Powerglides in Chevys, Torqueflites in Chryslers, and Fordomatics in Fords. As I recall, I also became probably the only mechanic in Los Angeles who could work on Packard Ultramatic transmissions, and those were the biggest, most complicated jobs there were. That also meant that I got to work on some of the fanciest cars in town, owned by some of the fanciest people. When I finished the course at the GM Training Center, I left the service station and opened a transmission repair shop. By that time I was making about $130 a week, which in late 1955 was pretty good money!"

As I listened to Joe describe his progress, his tones changed, and for the first time, I heard the sound of real pride in his voice, even now, sixty-odd years later. I have to say that in my own mind, it was pride he'd earned and deserved.

"That's quite a story, Joe! But tell me, were you happy out there in Hollywood? I mean you were three thousand miles from home and your family, and..."

"I was, and of course I missed my parents and my brothers and sisters. I was very happy that I'd been able to survive the journey across the country and begin making a life for myself, but as time went on, I did start feeling a growing desire to move back East. Home was still home, and I began to feel that the lifestyle in Hollywood was not so much for me. It was fun, and exciting, and certainly wilder than I'd been accustomed to back in Pennsylvania. The quieter attractions of home and family began tugging at me.

"In my second year in California, 1956, I was able to save enough money to take a trip back to Allentown to visit for the Christmas holidays. It was wonderful to see everyone, and they all wanted to hear about my journey and my adventures in Hollywood. When I got back to LA, I bought a much better car – a real step up for me. It was a '55 Cadillac Fleetwood with air conditioning."

Joe stopped here to gather his thoughts, while I took the opportunity to gather my own. His mention of moving his career forward started me thinking about my own career. I knew it was time for me to get serious about that, but while I was encouraged about my job at the supermarket, I definitely didn't think of roasting chickens and chopping celery for chicken salad as a career.

"Tell me, Joe…" I asked. "What direction did you have in mind for your career? What is it that got you up in the morning ready to put pedal to the metal, if you know what I mean?"

He smiled and closed his eyes for a moment.

"Good question! I think I've been fascinated with cars and trucks ever since I was very young. You have to remember that back before World War II, vehicles were a really important part of people's lives. Not only to get back and forth to work, but as kind of a badge of one's success. When I bought that Cadillac, for example, it changed the way people looked at me, and you can imagine it was a long way up the ladder from my broken down 1940 Ford and even from a '48 Ford convertible I'd bought when the first one died.

"I've been a worker, then later an owner of a service station in Allentown, then a worker again in a station in Hollywood. I'd taken those night classes at the GM Training Center and with my own homework tearing down and rebuilding junkyard transmissions, I'd become a pretty good walking-around expert on repairing and rebuilding automatic transmissions. That was a pretty big deal in those days. When a car's transmission broke down, it was inevitably the most expensive repair a driver would likely ever face, short of replacing an engine or buying a new car.

"I'd watched other transmission repair shops work, and learned a good deal about how *not* to do the repair jobs. I felt it was wrong to charge a hundred, two hundred, even up to nearly a thousand dollars to do a repair and short-change the customer by reassembling the transmission with junkyard parts, or parts half worn out by previous use, and then have the customer return six months or a year later for a second major repair. I believed there was a better way, a more honest and careful way to do the work and build trust in my customers.

"So if you combine my lifelong *interest* in cars with my passion to provide a better level of service to customers, I had all the motivation I needed to push ahead. When people around me began to notice my commitment to the career and to doing good work, they started supporting and helping me along."

"I see," I said. "...sort of. But I still don't get what you found so attractive about repairing people's cars and trucks. I mean it's not exactly brain surgery or running a national bank or something. Didn't you want something more?"

Joe stopped and looked hard at where my voice was coming from. For a minute I thought I'd just insulted him – again, and I felt my own face turn red.

"It seems that you've already built up some kind of 'work hierarchy' in your own mind, where some careers have more value than others, more honor than others, perhaps even more 'respectability' than others. I wouldn't be surprised if careers in which one sits in an office and wears a suit and tie every day is somehow more 'honorable' than careers in which men work with their hands and get dirty each day."

I wanted to stop him and shout "No, no! I didn't mean that! I just –"

But Joe wasn't going to be stopped, even by my interruption.

"If those are your beliefs, Ron, you're welcome to them. For me, providing a service that people need in order to carry on their own life, and are willing to pay for, has as much dignity and value as any surgeon, banker, or even priest. What adds value and satisfaction for me is providing that service with as much care, skill, professionalism and commitment to quality as I can.

"But let me answer what may be another side of your question. As I moved ahead, I learned more and more about providing the kind of repair services I believed in. It became clear to me pretty quickly that I could do more to provide those services as a business owner than I could as a mechanic working for someone else. So in that sense, I very much wanted 'something more' as you phrased it. Let me give you a few examples."

I breathed a sigh of relief and went back to listening.

"In 1955 and '56 I was a mechanic working in a Phillips 66 service station in Hollywood, then in my own transmission repair shop nearby.

"In 1957, in the spring, I learned that the 'Flying A' organization was planning to open a new station in Van Nuys, about twenty-five miles from my shop in Hollywood. By that time I'd made several friends in and around Hollywood, and not all of them were girls waiting for their big break on the movie screen. I had a good friend named Bob, who applied for a contract to buy and operate that station, but he didn't get it. He asked if I wanted to join him so that we could apply for the station contract together, and I jumped at the chance. I had experience as a station owner, and some small savings and no debts, although most of the money we needed for the station was Bob's. Together, our application was judged to be strong enough, so we got the station. I moved out to Van Nuys, rented another small apartment, and did only transmission repairs in one of the station's bays, mostly for about $150 per job. It was a good situation, a good job, with better money for both of us, and we were building a reputation as the best repair shop for miles around. All that and happily, nobody knew I was blind."

"What?"

"Well, I guess I need to remind you about the power of really serious concentration on my other senses, I never walked around with a white cane, and by focusing harder than most people could, I didn't expose my blindness by tripping over things on the station floor or having to touch thirty tools to find the one I needed. And yes, Ron, I took every customer on a short test drive in his newly repaired vehicle and never hit anything or anyone. As a matter of fact there was one customer test drive in which I had to slam on the brakes quite suddenly, putting my customer's face into the windshield. He didn't get injured, but he got frightened, and shouted at me with several four-letter words. It was only when he saw the little child, maybe nine or ten years old, who had ridden out into the street on his bicycle from between two parked cars, and who was standing inches from the customer's front bumper; that he uttered a few more exclamations, of a different type.

"You see, once again, it was echolocation working for me. I'd heard the bicycle's rattle as it ran over the curb on its way out into the street. It was a rattle I recognized instantly, having hear identical sounds from my own bicycle as a child."

"OK, OK!" I said. "Enough already! I'm ready to concede that Joe Cory, blind as a bat, was the safest driver from sea to shining sea, eyes or no eyes!"

He laughed at that, but only briefly, because on this issue, I had learned that this extraordinary man was thoroughly serious.

Chapter Sixteen

Homecoming

We were seated again in Joe's living room, while outside rain was coming down in buckets and barrels, punctuated by growls of thunder and bolts of an angry Mother Nature's high voltage. She must have been pissed, but inside we were dry and cozy.

As I had done a few times before, I started this session by summarizing where we'd been last time, to prove that I'd been listening carefully.

"So Joe, there you are in Van Nuys, the Crown Prince of Flying A, making a mint and fooling everybody about your physical capabilities and amazing them with your professional ones. What happened next?"

He smiled a warm smile, but thought for a moment before replying.

"Ron, we've been meeting together for quite a while now, and I've been telling you a good bit about my life. Your grandfather asked me to share it with you for a reason, so I'd like to hear from you. What difference is all this story-telling making for you?"

I hadn't thought about my grandfather's purpose in putting me together with Joe since we began, and beyond shaking me up and "getting me going" in my life, I'm not sure what his specific purposes were. I was suddenly a little uncomfortable, feeling like I was being "called to account"

138

and not knowing what to say. Still, the silence between us was lengthening, and I had to say something.

"Joe, I don't have an answer all put together to that question. I mean, your life has been a helluva story, your career as a hitch-hiker, and the job you've done coping with sudden blindness. There have been a couple of times when your story made me pretty ashamed of myself for feeling as bored with my life and as purpose-less as I have. I'd like to say that you've straightened me out and now I'm out there kicking ass and taking names, but I'm not sure I'm suddenly the happening person of the western world. I did go out and get myself a job, and I'm working at getting good at it. Once or twice it's occurred to me that you're pretty much a regular man, and not an Einstein or a Mike Trout, yet you've taken what life – or God -- handed you and made yourself at pretty damn good success, so if you can do it, maybe I should be able to do something myself, especially because I didn't get dealt the hand you got. I still don't think of myself as suddenly ready to poke myself in the eyes and stick my thumb out on Route 66, but…(suddenly I felt a flash of embarrassment that he would take those last words as an insult!) …well, does that answer your question – sort of?

"Sort of…" he said softly, and I'm not sure whose eyes you were referring to jut now, but…"

"-- Sorry Joe. That was insulting and I didn't mean it to be. It's just that --"

"—it's not a problem, Ron. And it was never my intent to make myself into some kind of hero or paragon just because I achieved some success despite going blind. I've never considered myself as any of that. In fact, in the first weeks and months after losing my sight I was thinking more about dying than living, as I believe I told you. It was my hope that my story would be helpful to you, perhaps encouraging you to see that whatever was holding you back from owning your own abilities and seizing your life's opportunity was in your mind, and nowhere else. If that hope failed, I'm sorry...

...but it's a sorrow I can survive."

The heat of his last words turned my embarrassment into a major California brushfire. I looked at the edge of the sofa cushion I was sitting on and wished I could crawl under it and hide.

"Joe, I'm really sorry, really. As I've listened to your story you've grown bigger and bigger in my mind, and at times that's made me feel smaller...and stupider. You have never bragged about a single thing in your story, never puffed yourself up or even considered your achievements as heroic, but we both know they are. Even as I've felt smaller and stupider, you were trying to tell me that I can accomplish things in my own life, that I can reach for the places you've been, the experiences you've had, maybe even the family you enjoy so much.

"I've made a start. No miracles, no twelve-point headlines, but it's a start, and I owe that to you and your story. Letting go of the traps I've built for myself isn't something I'm able to do all at once. One of my Mom's shrinks says it's a 'process – not an epiphany.'"

Joe laughed. "An epiphany! Wow, such a big word for such a 'small and stupid' fellow! Tell me, how far along are you in the 'process' of letting go of your own 'small and stupid' feelings?"

It was my turn to giggle. "If it's a twelve-step process, I'm somewhere between steps three and five I guess, but I'm definitely into the steps, OK?"

He smiled then and reached out his right hand. I had to get up and take a step to reach it with my own, and we held onto each other's hand for a moment. His smile poured a shower of water on my brushfire.

"OK then, you still want more?" he asked.

"I do, Joe. Hit it!"

"OK, then!" he said. "After working at our Flying A station in Van Nuys for over a year, I was feeling pretty good about things. I wasn't rich, by any means, primarily because I was spending as much time as possible dining and dancing with a good long line of those starlet wannabes. Even then, work and play took up all my waking hours, and in hindsight I'd have to say there weren't enough hours of sleep left over.

"In July, or maybe August of 1958, I got homesick again. Maybe it was the fatigue, maybe it was the speed with which money came in and went right back out, but the Hollywood lifestyle was becoming more the "Hollow-wood" lifestyle for me.

"In September, I told Bob I was leaving. It had been his money that got us the Flying A franchise, so there was no argument about dividing the business. Besides, he had a family, but no other job to go to, so I felt the station and all of the profits from the past year should be his. We agreed that I would take about $400 and head back east."

"By plane this time?" I asked.

"No. I'd sold the Cadillac, and while I had two suitcases this time, I hoofed it."

"No shit!? You hitch-hiked back across the country? You've gotta be kidding!"

"No joke. I have to admit, though, that my trip east was a great deal different. I was picked up by a fellow just east of Van Nuys in less than an hour after sticking my thumb out. He turned out to be a travelling salesman who'd spent a couple of months on the road and he wanted more than anything to get back home to St. Louis, to his family. He would drive until he had to stop for a short nap, and then drive on. Meals and tank fill-ups were as quick as possible, even though there were no McDonalds or other fast food places back then. It took us three days to get to St. Louis, and from its downtown station, I took a bus to Allentown, which took another two days. No sleeping outdoors, no bears, no wolves, and thank God, no snakes!"

"Well that was sure different!" I said. "And you didn't drive half-way to St Louis?"

Joe almost laughed. No, Ron, I didn't. Relax!

"By the time I got home, I had developed a pretty serious passion for owning my own business. The efforts I'd made in Los Angeles to become an expert in transmission repair and rebuilding had borne good fruit, and it had become important to me to be the best in the business, at least in my area. Part of that came because I'd spent time watching and talking to others doing the work, and I have to say I wasn't impressed with the way most of them went about their business. They took shortcuts and found ways to shave their costs but not their prices, which I found more than a little dishonest. I wanted to do better, to do it right, and to build the reputation that came with it."

"I can understand…" I said. "In my experience cutting corners and cheating customers has become the national pastime these days, in a whole lot of businesses."

Joe nodded. "I think I owe a great deal to my father, and even my brothers for my attitudes about doing business. Honesty was something I was taught from infancy. I wasn't only taught it, but my father modeled it himself in all his dealings with others. I'd also been taught to treat everyone with a measure of respect. That was drummed into us in Church and Sunday school, too. It occurs to me that virtues and morals and principles were different back then. Maybe it's just that they were more defined, more stable, and most people shared the same definitions. Anyway, these principles guided my personal life and my businesses.to me to do quality work and build a reputation as the best in the business.

"So I started my business, renting part of a building in town, half of which was a garage and half was a body shop. Actually, I took half of the body shop and opened a transmission repair shop. It seemed to me that I should take advantage of where I'd been and learned the business, so I called my shop "Hollywood Motors." That didn't hurt business at all!"

"I can just see it! I said. Joe Cory, movie star from LA -- with oily fingernails!"

He chuckled, and I was glad for that. I'd stepped over an invisible line with my humor, probably more than once, but when stayed on my side of the line, I could relax.

"Well, we did have Boraxo back then, and it did a great job on the oil and grease, but you get the picture. It didn't take long, however, before I felt another ambition rising…education."

"You own your own business and you're making good money being one of the best in town, and you want education? I don't understand!"

"It was a long time ago, Ron, and I'm not sure I can parse out my motives with precision, but I began to feel that a high school diploma wasn't enough. Part of it came from the fact that I was dealing with some pretty well educated customers, as well as suppliers, and my diploma was in a vocational ed program anyway. I had also harbored an interest in becoming a priest for a number of years, and more recently in becoming a lawyer, and a college education was a well-accepted prerequisite for both those vocations. Anyhow, I applied for admission to Muhlenburg College.

"And…?" I asked.

"And I got rejected."

"Really? Why?"

"The Dean of Admissions was both negative and dismissive. At one point he said the College 'didn't have time' to deal with a blind student. I persisted, and he came up with other reasons for rejecting me too, like the fact that my diploma was a voc. ed. diploma rather than a college prep diploma."

"So what did you do?"

"I went back the following year and pestered the Dean again, telling him that I really wanted to get a college education, that it was important to me, and that I would do the work and meet whatever standards the college had for its 'non-handicapped' students. But he rejected me again.

"The third year, in the summer, I went back one more time. This time I begged him to give me whatever admission test the college was using, and let me demonstrate by passing it that I could succeed as a student. After a good bit more resistance, he agreed, and asked the Head of the School's Psychology Department, Professor Walter Brackin I believe, to administer the test."

"And...?"

"And I passed it, of course. The Professor was sufficiently impressed to say I'll see you next semester."

About a month later, I received another rejection letter. I was shocked! I went back to the Dean's office and argued that I'd passed his entrance exam, but he didn't care. By this time, I think you can understand how utterly defeated, and frustrated I felt. On top of suffering another rejection, I felt totally powerless to do anything. As I walked out of his office, I had my head down and I wasn't concentrating on sounds around me as I had learned to do. When I got near the building's exit, I heard another person coming through the doors

"This was one of those moments when God must have taken a direct hand in my life."

"What makes you say that?" I asked.

"Because..." he said, "...the person I came face to face with was none other than the Head of the Psychology Department, Dr. Brackin. Before I knew it was he, he called me by name and asked me how things were going. I had to tell him I'd been rejected again.

"He grabbed my shoulder and said two things: 'Joe, don't worry about it for another minute. I'll take care of the Dean, and I'll see you in September.'"

I broke out in a grin of my own. I have to admit it. I love it when stories turn out like that.

Chapter Seventeen

Too Busy for Love

I was driving home from work the day after my last visit with Joe, and musing about the man, his story, and what had become something I never would have anticipated: a real friendship. I mean I'm still twenty-two, and a thoroughly modern Brant, and here I am anxious to sit down with him again to hear more details of a life that's gone on for eighty-two years! Who knew?

I should mention something – "driving home from work" now means something new for me. I have moved out of my parents' home, given up my hidey hole and my key to the family fridge, and am now in charge of doing my own dishes, dusting, swabbing out my own toilet, and generally living a life. I knew my parents had wanted that for quite a while, but when I finally announced that I'd found a place of my own that I could afford, my Mom was suddenly in tears about losing her dear son – for about twenty minutes. Anyway, they might have been tears of joy.

I have to say paying rent and food and gassing up my car is a pretty big deal for me, and it wouldn't have happened if I hadn't been called into the Manager's Office one day a couple of weeks ago for a one-on-one sit-down. I was more than a bit nervous when he called me, but when he told me what was on his mind, I got happy pretty quick, for a couple of reasons.

"You've been doing great work Ron, and I need to talk about your future," he'd said.

"My future?" (Uh-oh...here it comes.)

"Well, your near-term future anyway. We've got a major problem on our hands and I need your help."

Anxiety morphed into curiosity. "What kind of help?" I asked.

George Peterson is maybe forty, and while he's been with the company for a few years and risen to Manager pretty quickly, he's one of those super-motivated guys who's climbing the ladder as fast as he can.

"Well, you now that Martha is quitting. Her husband got himself a new job in Florida and Martha's been planning to move down there when she retires anyway, so she's out of here."

"Yeah, I heard."

"Well two other shoes have dropped. We're losing two more members of your department."

"Wow!"

"Yeah. Here's my problem. I'm responsible for the numbers this store puts up. Right now we're number nineteen out of thirty-two stores. I'm talking about sales plus customer satisfaction minus maintenance, food loss and labor costs. The Regional Office has given me a goal for this store's performance – to move from number 19 to the top 10."

"Wow!" (There it was, my favorite three-letter word again.)

"We're just about to close out the second quarter of our operating year, so we've got six months to raise sales, keep the customers smiling, lower our food loss…and keep our labor costs in line. That's where I need your help."

Sudden misunderstanding. "You mean you want me to take a cut in pay?"

Peterson smiled. "No, Ron. I want to give you a raise in your hourly rate as well as a significant raise in your weekly hours."

Brain freeze again. "Wow!" (Again…)

"Before you start dancing your way out the door, you need to understand what I'm saying here, OK? I need you to pick up you pace, shoulder more of the department workload, handle at least eight, maybe twelve over-time hours a week, and keep the customers smiling – and do it all with two fewer partners in the kitchen, maybe three. And I need you to keep it up for at least six months. If you can do that, you'll help me boost our bottom line by keeping labor costs down, and that, Ron, is how we move up the ranking."

I was careful to avoid a third "Wow!" in sixty seconds. I just nodded and wrestled with his message. Still, I was confused about one detail.

"But Mr. Peterson, why are you laying this on me? Crystal and Samantha have both been working here longer than me, and they know the operation better…"

"Believe it or not, Ron Brantley, you're the "rookie phenom" in the department. You've picked up on our work and our standards faster than anyone else, and from all appearances you've got the energy and focus to shoulder more responsibility. Crystal and Sam are great people, but they've both been here for a dozen years or more and for them, this is a job – not a career."

Our conversation went on for a couple of minutes, and I almost stumbled over a final "Wow!" as I walked out to my car. I was going to have to work harder—and longer, but my pay was going to nearly double, at least for six months, and suddenly there was still going to be folding money in my back pocket the day before my next paycheck hit my new bank account.

So now you know why I was particularly anxious to sit down with Joe Cory for another chapter in his life. I knew my Mom and Dad would be happy to hear about my increased work and pay, but it was Joe I most wanted to hear my news.

This time we met in slightly different circumstances. I joined him in a bakery/sandwich shop called "Sweet Treats" run by two Syrian brothers down in Lexington. Being blind, Joe was a bit hesitant in figuring out what to order for lunch – he didn't want something that presented too much challenge for a blind fork, so we both chowed down on gyro sandwiches on pita bread, which I really liked. Between bites, I told him my sudden bulletin, allowed myself to be momentarily drowned in his congratulations, and then asked him to pick up on his story.

"OK," he said. "I was back home, living in Allentown, running Hollywood Motors, which I'd expanded by taking over the space used as a body shop. I was beginning my studies at Muhlenburg as a full-time day student. To help me at Hollywood Motors I convinced my brother, Manny, to become my partner. He was a quick study and really helped me run the business when I was attending classes. In my junior year at Muhlenburg, we expanded the business further by adding a used car lot, where I worked selling cars in the evenings.

"That was 1961, two years before President Kennedy was assassinated. On the whole, I remember those days as going pretty well for me, except that I was burning my candle at both ends and in the middle, too. In addition to working both days and evenings at Hollywood Motors, I maintained a full academic schedule as a day-student in Psychology and Elementary Education – oh yes, and engaging in a pretty active social life on the side."

"I'd say that was a pretty full plate, Joe." (Actually, my head was spinning just imagining it!)

"It was, but back then I had the stamina for it, and was able to keep all my plates spinning. Studying wasn't easy, especially as I needed the help of readers whom I paid to read my text books to me. I also worked at learning braille, but few braille texts were available, and those that I could buy were more expensive than I wanted to cope with, so paying readers seemed like a more practical thing to do."

"Why Psychology and Elementary Ed? I mean how did that fit with transmissions and used car sales? I would have thought maybe business administration or something like that."

"Well, in the days after I had learned that Professor Brackin was going to take care of the Dean of Admissions' misgivings for me, I began thinking about what I wanted to study. At first, I thought about studying pre-law and becoming an attorney. Of course that would be a seven-year curriculum which felt like an eternity to me, but I entertained the thought anyway. But doing my business by day and carrying on my social life several evenings a week, I was able to meet several lawyers in and around Allentown and get to know them a bit. That was all it took to make me look elsewhere for my long-term career aspirations."

I chuckled at that, remembering a joke I'd heard in school. It said "the death of American society and culture occurred on the day we admitted our one millionth attorney to the bar."

"OK," I asked. "So why the two fields you mentioned?

Joe took a bite, chewed, and continued. "I'm sure you can understand that Dr. Brackin had become a genuine hero in my young life, and the thought of becoming his 'professional colleague' was quite attractive to me, at least emotionally.

"But I also learned from several people in the Psych Department that Pennsylvania, and indeed the whole country was experiencing a severe shortage of male teachers in elementary and secondary education, with obvious cultural consequences. So I felt that becoming a teacher might be a good way to serve the nation without putting on a uniform."

"It was about that time," he continued, "that something happened that changed the rest of my life."

I stopped chewing right then and held onto my still-spinning head. I didn't want to miss this.

"I've already mentioned that I enjoyed an active, and I'll even say quite successful social life in those years..."

"You stud you! So help me understand just what you mean by 'successful?'

152

Joe almost choked. "There you go again, looking for the sordid details. OK, so here's what I'll say about that, and no more.

"I was pretty consistently successful in hiding the fact that I was blind. There were plenty of clubs and bars and restaurants where I could meet young ladies, and plenty of places to dance. If you remember how blindness had forced me to rely much more on my other senses than sighted people, you can probably understand how I'd become a pretty skillful dancer. Many, -- in fact *all* of the women I met loved to dance, and I'm sure you've experienced that dancing, especially the slow dances to romantic melodies where the two of us touch each other closely and share whispers and so on, can lead to quick 'bonfires' of romance."

I racked my brains, but could recall very few dances, and no bonfires in my own life. Damn!

"In fact, Ron, I will tell you that I became extraordinarily sensitive to each woman I danced with – sensitive by touch for sure, but also by smell."

"Smell?!" It was my turn to choke.

"Smell. 'Scent,' if you prefer. But I found that after only a few minutes of slow dancing with a woman – any woman – I could detect a scent on her cheek, or her neck, that told me 'yes, there will be a bonfire tonight.'"

"Damn! You could really tell that?"

"I could," he said as he wiped his mouth.

I was seriously impressed, and determined right then and there that I was going to do my best to create a more sensitive nose right here in my own face!

"OK, I get the concept," I said. "So it was your nose that changed your life?"

Joe chuckled at that, and paused to take a draw on his iced tea.

"Close, but not exactly. Let me explain. When I went out to bars and clubs and dancing spots, I often stationed myself at the top of a stairway that led down to lower level rest rooms, which was always a good place to say hello to many, if not most of the women who were there.

"Sometimes we'd strike up a little conversation, and sometimes it led to a slow dance after her trip to the rest room. Now and then I'd sense an immediate connection, and push the envelope a bit, if you know what I mean."

Joe was suddenly narrating a movie and for a couple of minutes I actually closed my eyes to see the screen more vividly. I must have looked like a total weirdo to anyone eating at a nearby table.

"So one day, I think it was New Year's Eve, 1962, I was in one of the local clubs, and I'd stationed myself at my usual strategic spot. I'd said 'hello' to several women I knew at least casually, and invited one or two to dance when they came back upstairs.

"But there was one, a young woman I'd met three or four times before, though we hadn't shared any bonfires yet. When I noticed her approaching, I struck up another momentary banter, using all my well-oiled charm, and I remembered really enjoying our four-or-five minute conversation.

"I can't be sure now whether it was the occasion, just after midnight, which makes it the first moments of 1963, or that I was just feeling my oats that evening, but as she started town the stairs, I leaned over the railing, bent down and kissed her on the mouth. You've probably heard a thousand stories like this one, but suffice it to say she kissed me back, and when she did, she lit a fire that started in the hairs on my head and spread to the soles of my shoes.

"As I said, it changed my life."

It was my turn to take a slug of my drink, as much to cool me off as to slake any thirst.

Chapter Eighteen

Sleeplessness that Isn't Insomnia – Success that Isn't Just Hard Work

It was late evening when we were seated again in Joe's living room a few days later, and I have to admit that I was more than a bit tired. For the first time in my life, I was working pretty damn hard, and while I was grateful that Joe agreed to invite me over at different times to allow for my longer work schedule, I didn't want to fall asleep as he talked.

Joe asked me about my job and how it was going, and as usual, he was both enthusiastic and kind in his encouragement. It was funny. I had already felt, more than once, that I was getting more of that from Joe than I was getting from my own Dad, though I don't blame Dad for that at all. I guess it's just that I've been seeing more of Joe lately than I've been seeing of my own folks.

"So, back to my little autobiography, OK?"

"Yessir!"

"Funny!" he said. "I really should be writing this down. I can't tell you how many ancient memories have come bubbling up as we've been sitting together, memories I thought were long buried.

"Anyway, I think we stopped the other day with a single kiss, didn't we?"

I smiled at that. "We did, indeed! The mistletoe must have worked!"

He chuckled. "Well it *was* New Year's Eve, but I don't remember any mistletoe. Still, I remember quite vividly feeling that rush of heat from toes to nose, and as Jackie went down the stairs, I thought: 'Wow! That was...*interesting*!' I don't think I even danced with her later that evening, though I did dance with several other women, but thoughts about that kiss kept distracting me from those other dance partners.

"Was that it for you? You were hooked?" I wasn't sure I believed in storybook romances or love at first sight, even though "Princess Bride" and "Don Juan DeMarco" were two of my favorite feel-good movies. Still...

"No," he said after taking a moment to remember that moment again, a little smile on his face. "It was a very special kiss, different from all the others in some way, but I don't think I even saw Jackie for two or three weeks after that night. In fact, in the next year or so I even dated her sister for a bit.

Then, in November of '63, Jackie asked if I would help her to move her belongings to a new home she had decided to rent. I did help with the heavy lifting, and we began dating right after that.

In fact it was in that winter of 1963, on a ski trip, that Jackie first hinted that she was interested in me.

"Meanwhile, I was busier than a one-armed paper-hanger. Hollywood Motors was growing, and after a few months I expanded into half of that original building. Repairing and rebuilding transmissions was still the centerpiece of the business, but I had dreams and plans for more growth.

"Things carried on through the winter and spring with my work at the transmission shop, my studies, and my new steady date. In July, 1965, my father died suddenly, and my mother suffered a heart attack on the same day. It fell to me to take care of her, which I did for the next twenty-two years."

As you might expect, Joe's description of that event started me thinking of the day I would lose my parents, and I found myself sending up a silent prayer that I'd still have forty or fifty years before facing those events.

"So you can understand, Ron, the added chore of taking care of my Mom made my already full activity schedule a bit over-full."

"I can..." I said.

"So I decided to some time off from school, which meant I wouldn't graduate until 1966.

"Anyhow, my business kept growing. At one point in '65 I bought a lot downtown, and drew up plans for a building that was big enough to hold thirty cars. I'd been doing some stock trading on the side and some combination of luck and skill brought enough extra money in to pay for that land and other expansion of the business. Manny and I were working together and even though he was a lot more careful and conservative than I was, we had a good partnership going for quite a while.

"Our business was growing because of the way we worked. I was determined to do every repair the right way, and avoid the tricks other shops use to pad their profits, using old, worn, or second-hand parts while repairing only the one part that caused the transmission to fail. I always installed new clutches, brushes, bushings, pumps and gears when I did a transmission or engine repair, even though reinstalling old, worn, or junkyard components would have been invisible to my customers.

"I not only used new parts and components exclusively, but I learned pretty quickly which manufacturers produced the best components, and we used only those. We were not always the lowest price transmission repair shop, but nobody came back a week or a month after our job because their transmission broke down again.

"We also gave discounts on all jobs for retired and elderly customers, which most of our competitors did not."

"Excuse me, Joe. It sounds to me that you could have gotten away with some of those 'tricks of the trade' without anybody even knowing. Why the insistence on these practices even when you could have made more money doing business like your competitors?

Joe sat thinking about that long enough for me to begin worrying that my question had been insulting.

"Ron, I guess the short answer to your question is that we just thought it was the right way to do business.

"There is a longer answer, too, and I think it's just as important. I mentioned to you a week or so ago that I'd kind of fallen in love with cars back when I was a kid, even before high school. As I grew, I began to appreciate how important, even indispensable cars were to most families back then, and now, too. I also began to understand what a pain it was to the car owner, and even to his or her whole family, when the car broke down. If you live in downtown Manhattan or Philadelphia, you might be able to get to work, or even shop and get to doctors using public transportation, but in rural areas and places like Allentown and Emmaus, cars were a necessity, and when they broke down, most people were up a creek, if you know what I mean."

I knew what he meant. I'd spent a lot of time up there.

"Every repair job we did helped to solve a customer's problem, and often it was a paralyzing kind of problem, especially when the car owner wasn't also a shade-tree mechanic.

"When I started taking vocational ed. Classes in High School, I worked on car engines with a classmate. We were divided up into two-person teams. Inevitably, we felt ourselves becoming competitive with the other teams, getting jobs done right, and getting them done faster.

"That competitiveness continued when I went to work in that truck repair shop in Emmaus when I was fifteen. In California, even when I was just filling gas tanks and washing windshields, I 'watched' the mechanics working in the service bays and quickly figured out I could do the repairs they were doing and do them faster and better.

"When I was at that first Phillips 66 service station in Hollywood, I learned how doing quality work, doing the job right the first time and being efficient really did help grow the business and the shop's reputation. It became a matter of pride, and from then on it was really important to me to be the best in the business.

"But don't misunderstand, Ron. Being competitive, and being recognized as the best in the business wasn't just an ego trip. It was something I believed in. Along with honesty, and integrity, which I defined as delivering on my word, always. As I got older, I discovered something else. All of these principles, these ways of doing business – they all came from something even deeper, and maybe more fundamental. I loved my work. I loved cars and repairing them. I respected my customers, and it's probably not too much of a stretch to say I loved them, too. I cared about the people who worked for me, and I got a real sense of reward out of giving people work and a decent wage, plus a measure of recognition and praise for doing the work the way we wanted to do it.

"I hope you don't consider this to be bragging, or believing that I was better than anyone else. That was never part of it. Do you understand?"

It was my turn to take my time answering his question.

"I think, Joe, the most honest answer is that I do, but at this moment I understand it out here, on my surface. I expect that as I go on and get older, I'll understand it inside. I'd like to think that I could answer my own son, or grandson, if I ever have any, the same way you just did."

"Fair enough. Fair enough.

"Anyway back to ancient history. In 1966 I developed the concept of 'Auto-Tune Centers,' where we would expand beyond transmission repair to do tune-ups, electrical work, and air conditioning repairs, all of which were fast-growing areas of the auto repair business. By then I had three shops in Allentown, and I named them all 'Auto Tune Center' and planned to franchise them throughout Pennsylvania and the Northeast. That never did happen, primarily because the firm I was negotiating with wanted me to do all the travelling, franchise set-up, training, and so forth. That wasn't something I wanted. Four years of living three thousand miles from home and family had been enough for me and taking care of my Mom kept me close to home too. Neither did we ever build the larger building I had dreamed about on that downtown lot I'd purchased – there were just too many plates spinning – or balls in the air.

"Meanwhile, I added gasoline to all three of my shops, becoming ARCO and Exxon stations. I was full of ideas about growing the business, but my brother, Mannie made sure we managed our money as carefully as possible, paying off all our loans and mortgages, so that we weren't growing debt faster than we grew our little chain of repair shops.

So when the summer of 1966 rolled around, I could stand up at the graduation ceremonies at Muhlenburg and get my bachelor's degree. With that in hand, I could begin to think about slowing down enough to get a good night's sleep now and then, and even more important, I could ask Jackie to marry me. Our wedding was on August 19th of the following year, at the Syrian Christian Orthodox Church, and it was one of the happiest days of my life.

"No more burning the midnight oil listening to readers reading my textbooks and working to memorize as much of them as I could. I even used Jackie's help in learning French to meet the curriculum's language requirement.

"We had been dating exclusively since that ski trip in 1963, and under other circumstances I would have asked her to marry me back then. But I didn't want to have to add the

162

demands of marriage and starting a family in with my burnt-candle life. We talked about it, and she agreed to wait until I had graduated from college, which I did in June of 1966."

"Nice of her!" I said.

"It was, and I can only guess now that she agreed because she was really serious about me. She had a career of her own, first as a registered nurse and then as a certified anesthetist, while also working as a part-time professional fashion model, so she had her own busy schedule to contend with."

"Fashion model!? Wow!" I said, (and immediately started looking at Jackie more closely as she walked through the room. I was surprised at first, but the more I watched her the less surprised I was. She's one of those really good looking women who holds onto her beauty even into…well, I figured she had to be at least 75, which may even be beyond cougar age.)"

"Help me with something, Joe. I'm two and a half years into college, but with girls I kind of got left back…in kindergarten. Right now I'm not so much left back as left out: I can't support even a half-decent social life, much less a wife.

"What told you she was the one for you? I mean other than that first kiss – and what made you think you were ready to get married?"

Joe smiled one of those enigmatic smiles that suggested there was an "R" rated answer to my question, but I was only going to get the "PG" rated answer.

"She was shorter than me, and for some reason I was attracted more to shorter women than to the six-foot types. Unlike a lot of people, she never put on weight or got heavy, and while I figured it out by myself, plenty of other people confirmed then, and even today, she was – and is -- quite a looker.

"Remember, I could see just about normally until I was nineteen, so I'd examined a whole ration of young women, sometimes up close and personally, before my world went dark. As you can imagine, I had to use my other senses to learn about her beauty, but I have to say that I learned more about the beauty of her personality, and of her soul, just by spending time with her, than I did tracing her features with my fingertips."

That grabbed me, and for several minutes stopped me as I considered the notion of falling in love and appreciating a woman's beauty while being blind.

"So, there we were, August 1967, newly married and looking forward to starting a family. Both of us worked, and I knew Jackie had worked hard to get where she was in her career, so we waited for a short time before Jackie became pregnant – thus avoiding any scuttlebutt around town about p before w and shotgun weddings. But when we had our daughter, she was everything both of us and hoped for. When our son came along, he filled out our family foursome and we became a complete…and for me…a nicely symmetrical family.

"My business continued to grow, especially when I became a parts distributor for Chevron and then for Exxon, which brought in more money, of course, but also gave me a mission that my mind's special attributes could really absorb and succeed with. I had always been fascinated with the complexity of automobile engines and transmissions, and the more complexity the better I liked it. I think I probably memorized more part numbers, specifications, and qualities than anyone I knew of, and in hindsight, I believe I owe my success to that fascination and my ability to focus and concentrate my mind. That, of course, I believe I owe to sudden blindness and a journey across the country. I'm not sure I would have done as well if I'd kept my sight, strange as that sounds."

I thought about that, and while it sounded kind of weird, I could understand it, at least a bit. I have never seen blindness as a gift, but as I had listened to Joe's lifetime of success, it certainly seemed that he owed something to his blindness, for how it had helped to shape the sharpness of his other senses, and focus his concentration, probably well beyond what most of us achieve.

Still, my sense of Joe, which had grown through all of our visits, was that of a man who had been shaped from birth by a strong family, a set of beliefs about the necessity and the dignity of work, and even by his religion. I have no understanding of the Syrian Christian Orthodox Church, or even Catholicism, which I guess is its first cousin. Still, I believe that Joe Cory believes in God, his church, and the place it occupies in the center of his life. I remember how he described those moments on his journey across the country when he was totally lost, frightened to his bones, so cold and so alone that all he could do is fall down and beg for God's help.

It occurs to me that God didn't let him fail.

165

I'm at the beginning of my life as an adult – or at least an adult wannabe. I've felt pretty alone lately myself. I've blamed my parents, my schools, and even what's become of America. Be with me, too, God. I'm not blind, but there are a lot of things I haven't been able to see too clearly. I need your help!

Chapter Nineteen
Love and Business – A Helix

It was the end of Joe's story, and I knew, or at least my Grandfather believed that I should have been changed by it somehow. Some facts have changed. My parents' home is no longer my home. I have a job, even though I'm not ready to say it's a 'career' as my boss suggested. I even realized that I've been ignoring God in my messed up life, not that I'm a sudden Christian.

Still, I feel quite a bit like good old Ron Brantley. Joe's story has meant a great deal to me, and in a way he feels more like my brother than my grandfather, even though he'd qualify, age-wise. He's asked me to come over to his house today, for what I imagine could be the last time. Thinking about that, I'm not sure. As much as he's told me, and as much as it has meant to me, I don't want it to end. I still have questions.

I'm thinking about those questions as I drive toward his big brick fortress. They aren't small ones.

I parked my car in his driveway in front of his six garages (six!!) and walked down the hill toward his patio and rear entrance, so neither he nor Jackie has to come upstairs to let me in the front door.

He was waiting for me, as usual, and of course Jackie was preparing another festival of noshes, a kindness and grace that I'd enjoyed many times, and for which I wasn't nearly grateful enough.

"So…" he said, smiling. "…now you know my life. As others have said, 'it's my story and I'm sticking to it!' Have we done any good?"

I was instantly uncomfortable, and didn't want to have to answer that question right then.

"Joe, I'd like to say 'yeah, sure' but in some ways I feel like the jury's still out. I certainly don't feel like I'm suddenly Ron Brantley, Boy Wonder. In fact, I've thought about our whole sequence of sessions together, and while I've been amazed by your life, I still have some questions before I can sort out what it all means to me. Is it OK if we get to those?"

Joe sat back and closed his eyes for a moment, as if to consider what questions I might have after all that he had shared with me. When he opened them he looked in my direction and said:

"Sure. What's your first question?"

"First, I'd like to understand more about your thoughts, and even more, your feelings when you lost your sight at nineteen and made that insane decision to leave home and cross the whole damn US of A on your thumb and twenty-eight bucks. On the one hand, it seems like the dumbest decision a person could possibly make, but on the other hand, you made it, survived it, and lived to tell me about it."

Joe retreated again, as he had done a hundred times in our previous sessions. Eyes closed, he looked almost as if there was a time-travel synapse in his brain that took him back to the very moment of discovery of his blindness. When he came back, he spoke softly, as if his feelings from sixty-three years ago had come flooding back.

"Ron, I can barely find the words to describe my feelings of...well...of shame, depression, and real desperation. You remember I mentioned to you earlier that when I was a child I had to ask my mother for a nickel for a popsicle in the summer, but how much more it meant to me to buy my treats with my own money, money I'd earned from my paper route, and then from my job in Emmaus. Independence was precious to me, making my own way meant everything to me. There I was, suddenly dependent again, on my father who was ready to retire, and my older brothers and sisters. The thought of living on their charity for the rest of my life was...awful, terrible, and impossible.

"I just couldn't do it. I would rather die than put up with a lifetime of dependence as a blind man. But I couldn't just commit suicide, which was a mortal sin, so leaving, getting out on my own, away from Allentown, was suddenly absolutely necessary and I saw no alternatives whatsoever. I had no confidence that I would survive my trip, but dying on the road didn't feel like suicide. There was an almost frantic quality to my emotions, and once I settled on leaving and going out on my own, I couldn't wait to get on the road. Every day there in Allentown was just painful.

"It may not make sense to you, but I can feel those feelings even as I sit here today. "Do you understand?"

I nodded, then remembered Joe was still blind, so I spoke up.

"I do, Joe. In fact, it doesn't take much of my imagination to feel the very feelings that drove you so hard sixty-odd years ago."

"OK, then! Next question?"

"It seems to me that you were sustained, sometimes against all odds, either by incredibly good fortune, or by the Hand of God intervening on your behalf about a hundred times as you walked-hitched-stumbled-and damn-near crawled across the country. Which was it?"

Again, Joe was silent for a moment, his mouth turning upward into a gentle smile.

"You realize, of course, that's an impossible question to answer. I think I've shared with you that there were many, many times on my journey when I found myself in deep despair, depression, and total fear that I wouldn't survive the next hour. In every moment when I'd become totally lost, totally alone, often freezing, sometimes with no shred of sound to indicate human life around me, I looked upward and cried aloud: 'Where am I, dear Lord? And where are you?'

I couldn't have said it at each of those moments, but in the years since completing my journey, I've been more and more convinced that God was present in every one of those dark moments. I remember many nights going to sleep and being totally unsure that I would wake the next morning, so when I did awaken, I gave Him thanks just for being alive, and in those moments of giving thanks, I felt that my faltering faith was coming back.

"However, if you want to call it blind luck, rather than the presence of the Lord, you're welcome to that speculation."

Luck or God…I thought about that choice, and I have to admit that for me there was no clear answer, but the more I thought about it, the more I decided that 'blind' luck is harder to believe in than the presence of God in Joe's life...and maybe in mine.

Joe waited patiently through my reverie, finally reaching for his glass of wine.

"OK, Joe. Here's my next question. When you lost your sight, you seem to have reached inside and started to build up a set of skills that few of us mortals ever use, whether because you had to, to cope with blindness, or because you're just a really rare human being. How can I start to do something similar, without actually going blind, I mean?

He put his wine glass down and picked up a chunk of cheese and an olive, chewing slowly with his eyes closed again. The fact that he felt he needed to take time to think before answering came to me as something of a compliment, as in 'these are really good questions!'

"Ron..." he said finally, "...I'm not sure what day it was back in 1954 when I first found myself as blind as I am today, but I remember quite vividly that it was a real shock. Even in those first few seconds and minutes, I found myself listening to every sound around me, feeling every surface to locate myself and my surroundings. With every step I took I concentrated on the soles of my feet, trying to feel whatever was on the surface under me.

"I didn't recognize it at the time, but I was *concentrating* on those other senses, harder than I had ever concentrated before. When I got out of my sister's car and started walking west on Route 22, I recognized pretty quickly that I was going to have to learn to concentrate on capturing every shred of information coming to me through my senses as I had never concentrated before. As the days of my journey went by, I kept working on that ability, and I really believe it got stronger and stronger, just because it was so critical to my survival from one minute to the next. I can't say 'how' I developed my 'hyper-concentration' if I can call it that. I just did it.

"But there was something else that was involved in getting me across the country, and I can only describe it as a level of self-reliance that I'd never experienced before. I was absolutely alone on the planet for three and a half months, even when I was riding in a car driven by someone who was kind to hitchhikers. What I had feared most if I'd stayed home was a level of *de*-pendence that I just couldn't accept. What I experienced from the first moments on the road, was that I was totally, totally alone, with no one to depend on but myself.

"If you take those two items: concentration on my sensory capture of information, and my self-reliance, something strange has happened in the years since my journey. With each of those skills, as they grew, I used them and developed them for maybe forty, even fifty years. However, in the past ten or fifteen years, I've watched them begin to fall away with advancing age. I'm not as physically capable of moving through life on my senses as I used to be, and truth be told, I'm not as self-reliant as I used to be either. Just the other day, I walked out my front door for a short stroll as I've done a thousand times, but I got lost. I'm not sure how it happened, but I must have made a wrong turn, and suddenly I couldn't find my way back, and I was only a couple of blocks away.

It's a hard truth to accept, but perhaps God has a hand in that as well. I'm learning a degree of humility that perhaps I haven't had before."

It was my turn to reach for my wine glass, then a cracker and cheese, just to have something to do while I thought about Joe's answer. I was at the wrong end of my life to experience my skills, whatever they are, begin to fall away. I decided I could wait, even though that experience is probably inevitable in everyone's life.

"OK then! Here's another question: Once you got to California and settled into a less adventurous and traumatic life, you went to work with what quickly became a pretty serious passion, yet you did that in the business of auto repair, which doesn't strike me as worthy of a whole lot of passion. Why? What did it mean to you?

"That's an easier one!" he said. "Even when I was nine or ten, I remember being fascinated by mechanical things, and one of the first was the carburetor in my older brother's Model A Ford.

"Also, I described to you just the other day how important I felt cars had become to virtually every family's daily life."

I nodded, and once again remembered that nobody can hear a nod.

"I remember, Joe."

"Well, that's part of your answer as well. Next?"

I had to be careful with how I phrased this one.

"You were well blessed, I'd say, with good looks and personal style, and though you haven't wanted to "kiss and tell" as you put it, you certainly seem to have scored with the ladies...and then with one special lady. What's your secret?

This time there was little hesitation, but there was a wide smile on Joe's face.

"Ron, first, let me refer you to the Bible, to Paul's Second Letter to the Corinthians, where he makes perhaps the most powerful description of love I've ever read. My own habits are less poetic, even less sophisticated...and there should be no 'secret' about them.

"I'm *interested* in women and I make it my business to demonstrate it immediately. An older and wiser man than me once said: *If you want to impress a woman you've just met, start a conversation by asking her an open-ended question about herself, and then shut up!* It's damn good advice!

"As she answers your open-ended question, listen, but listen very carefully. Pay attention! The more interested you are in her, the more interesting she'll think you are.

"Yeah, I understand, Joe..." I said. "But what about when we get beyond conversation and stuff?"

He giggled. "There you go again, wanting to get to the kiss-and-tell stuff. I have only one piece of advice. Serve her, please her first, before you worry about taking your own pleasure. Is that clear enough?"

It was.

"Got any more?" he asked.

"I do, and you might say this one is related to the last one. You said, and I believe you, that you've been stone in love for damn near fifty years. I can see how true that is, just watching you and Mrs. Cory during our visits. That's an achievement all by itself that few people can claim these days. How do you explain that, especially given the current 54% divorce rate?

"Hmm," he said. "That's a little more complicated. First of all, you have to know that in forty-nine years and ten months, Jackie and I have had a pretty normal share of conflicts, misunderstandings, little moments of temper and disagreement – perhaps even more than most married couples, because of the burden my blindness places on Jackie's shoulders. But we have both been dedicated, from day one, to maintain a constant, abiding love for each other. Both of us both tolerate our personal differences, little habits and idiosyncrasies that might irritate us. With all of that, our love just abides.

"But Ron, an important part of staying in love is our priorities. Each of us believes that what we give in our relationship is more important than what we get. The minute either one of us were to start counting or measuring our own satisfactions against our own desires, we would start to kill our relationship.

"You'll find as you get on with your life that the good feelings you feel when you're making someone else happy, or satisfying someone else's need or desire...those feelings rise in you faster, more simply, and even more automatically than the more complicated feelings you get when you receive gifts or kindnesses or love from someone else. You may not believe this, but pay attention to the way this principle works in your life. You'll notice it pretty quickly."

He stopped there and was silent for a minute, a smile slowly forming on his face.

"I still get a flush of warmth every time Jackie is near me, or enters a room where I am, or holds my hand, or speaks my name…even to this day."

I felt I ought to be taking notes, but it was too late for that. I was suddenly a little worried that I would forget Joe's answers to these questions of mine, and I didn't want to do that.

We took a break just then to sit down to Mrs. Cory's latest table-full of refreshments. There were at least a dozen different plates of things cooked and warm, raw and chilled, and another bottle of prosecco, which I had never tasted before meeting the Corys but now enjoyed a whole lot!

Joe explained to Jackie that I was peppering him with questions, and he added: "they aren't small ones."

"And you're being the 'Answer Man'?" she asked. "What a challenge for you, dear!"

He reached for her, but could only swat air, as they both laughed.

"OK, smartypants!" he said. "You sit here with me and help me with the rest of them!"

I only had two more, and I was glad to have Jackie's thoughts as well as Joe's.

"What's your next question, Ron?" she asked as she sat down between us.

"Well," I said, trying to phrase the next one and finding it difficult.

"-- Going back to your childhood in Allentown and wintertime baths in the kitchen because there was no central heat, and carrying through your whole life, it seems clear you've been guided by a set of principles, beliefs, morals, standards, or even just manners. Where did they come from? Was it your religion? Your parents? Or just the way things were back then?

Joe answered first. "All of the above! My parents were certainly great role models and teachers of a lot of fundamentals like respectfulness, manners, kindness to strangers, especially those who had less than we had, and so on..."

Jackie spoke up just then. "Something else was different then, too. Our neighborhood was full of people from different countries, different cultures, people who spoke different languages and worshipped in different churches. People who lived in the wealthiest parts of town may have felt superior to us because of their wealth, but those of us who were working hard to climb the ladder learned to respect one another, even becoming friends and sharing with one another in hard times. It feels a bit different today, although I suspect it doesn't have to be."

Joe finished a bite, took a sip of his prosecco, and said "You know I don't think we're charging this young man nearly enough for all this good advice!"

We all laughed, although it occurred to me that he was more right than wrong about that.

"OK, I agree. I have only one more question, if you'll permit...before you hand me your bill."

Jackie smiled and reached for my hand. "Not to worry, Ron. Our fee would only kick in if you had *two* more questions!"

"Phew! I said. All right, here's my last question, I promise. I have no desire to rebuild transmissions or distribute auto parts. But I would like to be as successful as you have been in your business and your family happiness. I'd really even like to have a place like this one day. What do I need to do to get on that path?"

Joe laughed, and Jackie joined him. I didn't realize that there was anything funny about the question, but I waited.

"Ron," Joe began. "—First of all, be careful what you wish for. We've been trying to sell this house for more than a year now, and get something much smaller and simpler. It's been wonderful to live here with my daughter, her husband and our grandchildren, but they're moving away now and this beautiful house is rapidly becoming a bit difficult for the two of us to manage."

Jackie took his hand just then, and he must have felt that rush of warmth. After a moment, he continued.

"But in a more direct answer to your question. I would say get to know yourself. I know you've had some negative feelings about your own life so far, but let me assure you from the deepest part of my own belief: God forgives me, and you, and all of us, every day, for every fault and failure and mistake that we make. Look at how many of my own personal stupidities you noted in my trip planning sixty-odd years ago, and He not only forgave me for them, He also saved me from their consequences. So if He is busy forgiving you for all your real and perceived inadequacies, you'd better get busy forgiving yourself, and beginning to believe that there's nothing you absolutely can't do if you keep learning, working, and giving thanks. Finally, I think I would add – be interested…about yourself, about others, and about the millions of things going on around you.

"Whatever you end up doing to support yourself, and eventually your family, bring your interest, your curiosity, and most of all, your love to whatever you have chosen to do. Do that, and whether you earn a few thousand or a few million, you'll be successful…and people around you will love you…even as we do!

When I said goodbye to Joe and Jackie on the front porch of their brick fortress, we hugged, and I remembered Joe's memory of the hug from his father when he left home on that insane, incredible trip across the country so many years ago.

Funny. I'm just now starting out on my own trip. I'm blessed with all my senses, but to make my life work half as well as Joe's, I think maybe I'll need to work on developing my own kind of "echo-location" – at least to hear the echoes of his story and the lessons they have for me.